OVER 120 QUIZZES FOR ALL OCCASIONS

A Source Book of Bible Quiz Ideas
Rachel Green

SCRIPTURE UNION

130 City Road, London EC1V 2NJ

© Scripture Union 1980
Reprinted 1981, 1983
ISBN 0 85421 799 1

Printed and bound in Great Britain
at The Pitman Press, Bath

INTRODUCTION

'Not another quiz book! There are too many already!' Is that your reaction? But Quizzes for all Occasions is not just another quiz book — packed with useless information, pointless questions, impractical ideas and obscure names. It is a source book of 20 quiz ideas *and* a source of actual quizzes. The actual quizzes are detailed examples of the ideas, and cover a wide range of Biblical topics — including Bible background, books, events, objects or animals, people, places, themes or verses.

No quiz ideas or actual quizzes have been included unless they can satisfy one or more of the following criteria:
* suggest ways of discovering/sharing Bible truths in a way that children and adults can enjoy together;
* provide an exciting way of revising what the children already know;
* stimulate children to think about what they know and to discover new, important, relevant truths;
* help children to feel more 'at home' with the Bible because they know their way round it better.

In addition, quiz ideas and actual quizzes must be practical. Every effort has been made to ensure that all the quizzes in this book actually work. Many have been tested by experience and found to be usable and effective.

To help the leader, answers or solutions and Bible references have been included with most quizzes — wherever possible on the same page. The version used throughout is 'The Good News Bible, Today's English Version' published by Collins. This version is intelligible to children and also contains maps and pictures. Whenever Bibles are used for quizzes, it is essential that children should have access to the same version — preferably (as far as this book is concerned) The Good News Bible version.

Age-groups are also suggested for each quiz idea and actual quiz. Please use these as guidelines only. No two groups are the same and leaders should look at the contents and judge for themselves. Leaders who are organising a quiz for mixed age-groups should select relevant material for each age-group represented and arrange their own quizzes.

As well as quiz ideas and actual quizzes, this book contains a list of useful addresses and sources of books and audio-visual materials. This list will be particularly useful to those preparing musical quizzes or those requiring writing or drawing materials. You will certainly need at least one of the following (when working together in one large group):

* blackboard and chalks;
* whiteboard and suitable pens/markers;
* acetate sheets, soluble pens/markers and an overhead projector;
* large sheets of card (or paper over board) and thick-nibbed felt pens.

For individual working you will need:

* paper, pencils and colouring materials.

Some may be concerned about the use of the pronouns 'he' or 'him' throughout this book. Let me assure you that this is for convenience only: absolutely no male chauvinism is intended!

Quizzes may be useful in one of the following: Sunday schools; Bible classes; clubs; after-church fellowships; beach missions; Scripture Union meetings; Bible studies; socials; Christian holidays/house parties; family services.

A quiz may be used as an introduction, a conclusion or as the main part of a programme.

Try one out soon!

Rachel Green

CONTENTS

1. QUIZ IDEA

ANIMAL, VEGETABLE OR MINERAL

The children can choose any Bible person, object, place or a combination of these. One child leaves the room while the rest make their choice. The child who has gone out returns, and asks a maximum of twenty questions, requiring 'yes' or 'no' answers only. If he guesses before he has asked twenty questions, he wins; otherwise the panel wins.

Give several children a chance to beat the panel.

Age Group: Seniors

Examples: Jonah's whale — (Jonah 1:17 — 2:10)
the snake that bit Paul (Acts 28:1—6)
Barnabas (Acts)
King Ahab (1 Kings 16:29 — 22:39)
Balaam's donkey (Numbers 22:22—35)
Naboth's vineyard (1 Kings 21)
the five loaves (John 6:1—14)
Noah's Ark (Genesis 6—9)
the gold bull (Exod. 32)
the idol Dagon (1 Sam. 5:1—12)
Goliath's sword (1 Sam. 17)
Solomon's Temple (1 Kings 6)
the axe head that floated (2 Kings 6:1—6)
Jonah's plant (Jonah 4)
Amos' basket of fruit (Amos 8:1—3)
the manger (Luke 2:1—7)
the paralysed man's bed (Luke 5:17—26)
the Good Samaritan's first aid kit — bandages, oil and wine (Luke 10:25—37)
the unfruitful fig tree (Luke 13:6—9)
the sycamore tree that Zacchaeus climbed (Luke 19:1—9)
the wine at the wedding in Cana (John 2:1—12)
the Cross (John 19:17—42)

2. QUIZ IDEA

'CHOOSING' QUIZZES

The children are asked a question and given a choice of answers, one of which is correct. They can indicate the right solution by underlining, colouring, ticking, encircling, pointing out or calling out the correct words, numbers or pictures.

Age Groups: Primaries, Juniors, Seniors

Examples: a. **Choose the right occupation**

Preparation: Have a copy of the questions, answers and references below.

Organization: Work together or divide the children into two teams, offering alternate questions to each team.

For: 7's to 11's

1. Was Andrew a fisherman, a shepherd or a tax-collector? (fisherman – Matthew 4:18)
2. Was Jonah a fisherman, a tent-maker or a preacher? (preacher – Jonah 1:2)
3. Was Naaman a doctor, a cup-bearer or a soldier? (soldier – 2 Kings 5:1)
4. Was Abel a priest, a shepherd or a gardener? (shepherd – Gen. 4:2)
5. Was Pharaoh's servant, who was hanged, his baker, gardener or wine steward? (baker – Gen. 40:22)
6. Was Solomon a sailor, doctor or king? (king – 1 Kings 2:12)
7. Was Matthew a fisherman, a tax-collector or a tent-maker? (tax collector – Matt. 9:9)
8. When the Israelites were in Egypt were they shepherds, slaves or musicians? (slaves – Exod. 2:25)
9. Was Eli a prophet, a carpenter or a priest? (priest – 1 Sam. 2:11)
10. Was Boaz a soldier, a farmer, or a doctor? (farmer – Ruth 2:3)

b. Choose the right picture

Preparation: Make an enlarged copy or sufficient duplicated copies of the pictures and writing below. The children will need colouring materials.
Organization: If you have a small group, make this an individual quiz. If you have a large group, work together on the enlarged copy, or compete in teams.

For: 5's to 7's

The Crippled Woman (Luke 13:10–17)
One day Jesus healed a woman who had been bent over for eighteen years. At last she was able to stand up straight.

Colour in blue the things the woman saw when she was bent over. Colour in green the things she could see after Jesus had healed her.

ANSWERS: Colour sandal, ladybird and worm in blue; face, sun and tree in green.

10

For: 7's to 11's

(i) Children and parents
'Respect your father and your mother' (Exod. 20:12).

Colour the speech bubbles which show children obeying this command.

ANSWERS:
(i) Colour speech bubbles in B, D, H.

For: 7's to 11's

(ii) Christian thoughts (Philippians 4:8)
'Fill your minds with those things that are good and deserve praise: things that are true, noble, right, pure, lovely and honourable. (Phil. 4:8)
    Put a large cross through the pictures in which the children are not thinking the thoughts mentioned in the verse.

ANSWERS: (ii) Cross out B, C, D, F.

For: 7's to 11's

(iii) Events in Peter's life

Tick the pictures which show events in Peter's life, or events at which he would have been present.

ANSWERS: (iii) Tick A, B, E, F.

c. Choose the right version of a story

Preparation: This can be a written or verbal quiz. If written, hand out duplicated copies of the story, or write it up on a board, or on an acetate sheet, for an overhead projector. Alternatively, have one leader's copy for reading aloud.

Organization: Working together, or competing in teams, let the children call out, underline, tick, encircle, or colour round the right words.

For: 5's to 7's

Bible Animals (large pictures of the animals can be shown)

1. On Palm Sunday did Jesus ride a horse, a camel or a donkey into Jerusalem? (donkey — Matt. 21:5)
2. Did Noah send a robin, a dove, a sparrow, a raven or an eagle out of the Ark? (raven and dove — Gen. 8:7,8)
3. Did David once kill a bear, a wolf or a tiger? (bear — 1 Sam. 17:36)
4. When the Israelites crossed the water, were they being chased by people on donkeys, horses or camels? (horses — Exod. 14:9)
5. In Jesus' story, did the boy who went away from home get a job feeding pigs, rabbits, or cows? (pigs — Luke 15:15)
6. Did Jesus tell another story about a lost horse, a lost cat or a lost sheep? (sheep — Luke 15:4)
7. Did Jonah spend three days in a snake, a fish or a dog? (fish — Jonah 1:17)
8. Did Pharaoh dream about seven fat and seven thin cows, mice or sheep? (cows — Gen. 41:2,3)
9. Did a donkey, a snail or a snake speak to Eve in the garden of Eden? (snake — Gen. 3:1)
10. Was Daniel put in with rats, lions or elephants? (lions — Dan. 6:16)

For: 7's to 16's

(i) Peter and Cornelius (Acts 10)

In Caesarea there lived a man called Cornelius who was a *high priest/captain* in the Roman

15

army/navy. A *soldier/angel* told him to send men to *Joppa/Jerusalem/Jordan.* Meanwhile *Peter/John/James* had had a vision of a *blanket/sheet/tablecloth* full of *feathers/living creatures/people.* The *sheet/blanket/tablecloth* was lowered *four times/twice/three times.* The messengers *invited Peter/James/John to Cornelius' house/attacked Peter/James/John.* When he arrived at Cornelius' house he found *Cornelius by himself/sick people waiting to be healed/many people.* He told the Gentiles that he now realised that *only Jews were accepted by God/God had no favourites/the good news about Jesus was for everyone.*

For: 7's to 16's

(ii) The Good Samaritan (Luke 10:25–37)
Jesus told the story of the Good Samaritan in answer to the question *'What must I do to be saved?'/'Who is my neighbour?'/'How often should I forgive others?'* The traveller was going from *Jerusalem to Jericho/Tyre to Sidon/Egypt to Canaan.* On the road robbers *killed him/beat him/stripped him.* The man who helped the wounded traveller was *the Levite/the priest/the Samaritan.* The third man who came along felt sorry for the wounded man and *went past/tended his wounds and took him to an inn/went to fetch help.*

d. Choose the right verse ending
Write out the beginning of some verses and three or four possible endings, only one of which is correct.

For: 7's to 16's

John 14:6
Jesus answered him, 'I am the way, I am the truth, I am the life . . . *love one another/I did not disobey the vision I had from heaven/no one goes to the Father except by me/I will ask the Father and he will give you another helper.'*

16

e. Choose the right reason

Preparation: Think about why certain Bible events happened and offer various reasons for the children to choose from. Have a list of the questions and answers.

Organization: Work as one group or divide the children into competing teams.

For: 7's to 11's

1. Was Daniel put into the lions' pit
   i. because he would not bow down to Nebuchadnezzar's statue
   ii. because he prayed to God
   iii. because he was training to be a lion-tamer?
   (Dan. 6:11,12)
2. Did Mary pour perfume on Jesus' feet
   i. because it was the custom to do this to visitors
   ii. because Jesus expected all his followers to do this
   iii. because she loved him?
   (John 12:3,7)
3. Did Jonah spend three days and nights in a whale
   i. because it was a quick way to cross the sea
   ii. because he did not go to Nineveh as God had told him to do
   iii. because he disobeyed the king?
   (Jonah 1:2,3,12)
4. Was Mary Magdalene sad
   i. because Jesus' body was missing from the tomb
   ii. because the angels frightened her
   iii. because Peter and John had left her behind?
   (John 20:13)
5. Did Peter say three times that he didn't know Jesus
   i. because Jesus had told him to
   ii. because all the other disciples had said the same
   iii. because he was afraid?
   (Matt. 26:69–75)

6. Did Moses put a metal snake on a pole
   i. so that the people could worship it
   ii. so that those with bites could look at it and be healed
   iii. so that snakes would crawl up it?
   (Num. 21:8)
7. Did Jesus cry
   i. because his friend Lazarus was dead
   ii. because he had so few friends
   iii. because he was too late to heal Jairus' daughter?
   (John 11:33,35)
8. Did Rebeccah put skins on Jacob's arms and neck
   i. to keep him warm
   ii. to make him look like a goat
   iii. so that he would feel hairy like his brother Esau?
   (Gen. 27:11,16,22)
9. Did Joseph's brothers sell him
   i. because he wanted to go to Egypt
   ii. because they hated him and his dreams
   iii. because they needed the money?
   (Gen. 37:4,8,20,27)
10. Did God lead the Israelites through the desert for forty years
   i. because that was the shortest route to Canaan
   ii. because he wanted to see whether they would obey him
   iii. to teach them to obey him
   iv because he hadn't chosen which country would be theirs
   (Deut. 8:2,16)

f. **Other choosing quizzes**
Only five different 'choosing' ideas have been suggested; there are many others you could prepare to suit the needs of your group.

18

3. QUIZ IDEA
DRAW THE ANSWER QUIZZES

You can devise these on any drawable Bible background theme, Bible book, event, object, animal, person, place, verse or theme. It is a particularly suitable quiz for children who have writing and reading problems.

Age Groups: Juniors, Seniors

Examples:

> **For:** 7's to 16's
>
> **a. Joseph sold into Egypt (Genesis 37)**
> *Preparation:* Have a copy of the questions, answers and references below. If you have a small group and want them to work individually, give each child a pencil and duplicated copy of the quiz with spaces for his drawings. If you are going to work as one group have ready suitable writing implements and a large sheet of card or paper, black or white board, or acetate sheet and overhead projector.
> *Organization:* Unless the children are working individually, read out each question and let a child volunteer to come up and draw the answer.
> 1. What special garment did Joseph receive from Jacob? (long-sleeved coat — v.3)
> 2. What did Joseph's brothers look after? (sheep or goats — v.12)

3. What bowed down in Joseph's first dream? (sheaves — v.7)
4. What bowed down in Joseph's second dream? (sun, moon and stars — v.9)
5. Into what did Joseph's brothers put Joseph? (well — v.24)
6. What did the brothers sell Joseph for? (bag of money or twenty coins — v.28)
7. What animals were loaded with spices and resins? (camels — v.25)
8. What did Joseph's brothers kill? (goat — v.31)
9. What were Joseph's brothers doing when they saw the Ishmaelites coming? (eating food — v.25)
10. What did Jacob think had killed Joseph? (any wild animal — v.33)

For: 10's to 16's

b. Well-known sayings

The aim of this quiz is to make children think about the use of metaphor and 'picture language' in the Bible. It would be a good introduction to a lesson on the wind and fire of the Holy Spirit at Pentecost.

Preparation: Have a list of well-known metaphorical phrases e.g.

I've got butterflies in my stomach
It's raining cats and dogs
Looking at the speck in your brother's eye
He's got his head in the sand
He's got a screw loose
A camel through a needle's eye
She's walking on air

Organization: Divide the children into groups. One member of each group comes to you to be told the first saying. He has to draw this while the rest of the group guess the real meaning of the saying (e.g. 'I'm frightened' for 'butterflies in my stomach'). The group member who guesses the meaning comes out to you for the next phrase. The winning group is the group who gets through the list first.

20

4. QUIZ IDEA
GUESSING FROM CLUES

You can devise guessing quizzes about Bible background, books, events, objects or animals, people, places, themes or verses. Prepare one, two, three or more clues.

Organization: The children can be divided into teams. For half points older children can look up the answers in the Bible.

Age Groups: Primaries, Juniors, Seniors

Examples:

For: 5's to 7's

a. Bible objects in the life of Jesus

1. Guess what I'm thinking of: it's big and made of wood and it floats. Jesus once fell asleep in one. (boat)

2. It's lovely and cool when you're hot, and very useful when your're thirsty or dirty. You can drink it and one day Jesus turned six big, stone jars of it into wine. (water)

3. It grows out of the ground and is tall and shady. Zacchaeus climbed into one of these to see Jesus. (tree)

4. It's big and round and holds something we all need every day. Women went to it each evening and dipped their jars into it. Jesus once sat beside one and talked to a sad woman. (well)

5. It's useful and made of cloth. Once Jesus put one round himself to dry his friends' feet. (towel)

6. We have it for tea and it can be white or brown. Jesus once used five small loaves of this to feed 5,000 people. (bread)

7. I hope you comb this every day! Jesus said that God knows how many of these you have on your head. (hair)

8. Perhaps you use one at the seaside. Some of Jesus' friends were mending theirs when Jesus called them to follow him. (net)

9. It belonged to Jesus. When Jesus was dying, soldiers threw dice to see who could have it. It

was made of one piece of woven cloth with no seams. (robe)

10. It helps us to see at night. Jesus is like one. (light)

For: 5's to 7's

b. Who am I? (rhyming clues)

1. I didn't do what God had said,
I ran away to sea instead. (Jonah)

2. A fisherman I used to be,
A clue — my name begins with 'P'. (Peter)

3. I had a special coat from Dad,
Because I was his favourite lad. (Joseph)

4. In a garden I felt sad,
Till Jesus spoke and made me glad. (Mary)

5. An angel promised me a boy,
Who'd bring to all the world great joy. (Mary)

6. In the Temple I went to stay,
There God spoke to me one day. (Samuel)

7. I heard that Jesus would be here,
I climbed a tree so I'd be near. (Zacchaeus)

8. Once a princess saw me float,
In my little basket-boat. (Moses)

9. In a garden I did wrong,
When a serpent came along. (Eve)

10. God told me to build a boat,
My, you should have seen it float! (Noah)

For: 7's to 16's

c. Bible Books

1. A girl's name (Ruth/Esther)

2. Sought when unemployed (Job)

3. Only partly warm (Luke)

4. Men who preside over courts (Judges)

5. A going out (Exodus)

6. A boy's name (Samuel/Timothy/Titus/James/Peter/Joshua/Matthew/John/Jude/Luke/Mark)

7. Sections of a play (Acts)

8. What mathematicians deal in (Numbers)

9. Weeping and wailing (Lamentations)

10. They wear crowns on state occasions (Kings)

22

11. Wise sayings (Proverbs)
12. Historical stories (Chronicles)
13. Now listen to my tale of someone and the whale (Jonah)
14. They were very good at central heating and conquered Britain a long time ago (Romans)
15. Another name for Jewish people (Hebrews)
16. Something that is shown to someone (Revelation)

For: 7's to 16's
d. Who was he? (one clue)
1. He was on his way home with Jesus when his servant brought him some bad news. (Jairus — Luke 8:49)
2. An angel told him to speak to a man in a desert (Philip — Acts 8:26)
3. He ate wild honey and part of him ended up as a present for a dancing girl. (John the Baptist — Matt. 3:4; Mark 6:21–27)
4. His knees knocked and he went very pale at a feast. (Belshazzar — Dan. 5:1–6)
5. Many poor people at Joppa knew her. (Dorcas — Acts 9:36)
6. He rebuilt the walls of a famous city when they had been broken down. (Nehemiah — Neh. 2:17)
7. He ran away from his Christian master, then met another Christian. (Onesimus — Philemon 15,16)
8. Jesus cried because of him. (Lazarus — John 11:35–37)
9. When he was seventy-five, God wanted him to go on a long journey. (Abraham — Gen. 12:4)
10. After letting his special clothes be put on his son, he died on a mountain. (Aaron — Numb. 20:28)

e. Who was he? (three clues)
Award three points for guessing correctly after the first clue, two points after the second clue and one point after the third clue.

23

For: 7's to 11's

1. He was a murderer. A crowd of people wanted him to be set free from prison. Jesus was handed over to be crucified when he was set free. (Barabbas)

2. He became David's enemy. He was the first king of Israel. His son was David's best friend. (Saul)

3. He was one of Pharaoh's officers. He put Joseph in charge of his house. His wife had Joseph put in prison. (Potiphar).

4. He had twelve sons. He pretended to be his brother. His favourite son was sold into Egypt. (Jacob)

5. He was related to Jesus. He wore clothes made of camel's hair. He baptised Jesus. (John the Baptist)

For: 11's to 16's

1. He said he was too young when God called him. A book in the Old Testament bears his name. A king once threw a scroll he had dictated on to a fire. (Jeremiah)

2. He fought against the Midianites. He had in his army only the three hundred who lapped the water. He 'tested' God by putting wool on the ground. (Gideon)

3. He was one of the twelve apostles. He wrote five New Testament books. He once volunteered to call fire from heaven on some Samaritans. (John)

4. He is mentioned in each of the four gospels. He was a Roman governor. His wife had a bad dream about Jesus. (Pilate)

5. He was successor to Felix. He was visited by King Agrippa. He said to Paul, 'You have appealed to the Emperor, so to the Emperor you will go.' (Festus)

5. QUIZ IDEA

MIMING AND ACTING QUIZZES

These are mainly verbal quizzes, though sometimes some writing is necessary or helpful. Children can compete in teams or work individually or together. The children will need to read in their Bibles about the events they intend to present.

These are popular quizzes where you have a lively, extrovert group.

Age Groups: Primaries, Juniors, Seniors

Examples: **a. Guess a Bible person**

Preparation: You will need a list of the subjects, Bible references, and some ideas for miming in case the group members dry up.

Organization: One child will mime to the rest. Whoever guesses scores a point. Or divide the children into two teams. Give each team a piece of paper with five of the subjects written on it. One team mimes for the other. If the mime is guessed the guessing team wins a point.

For: 5's to 7's

1. David (mime putting stone in sling and aiming — I Sam. 17:49)
2. Noah (mime hammering and building the ark — Gen. 6:14)
3. Jesus (mime beckoning Zacchaeus from the tree — Luke 19:5)
4. Shepherd (mime looking for lost sheep, finding it and carrying it on shoulders — Luke 15:1–7)
5. Moses (mime being dazzled by burning bush, and taking off shoes, or stopping the water of the Red Sea — Exod. 3:2,5 or Exod. 14:21)
6. Peter (mime fishing and pulling in net — Matt. 4:18)
7. Sower (mime holding container of seed in one hand and scattering seed with the other — Luke 8:5)
8. Priest (mime walking round wall of Jericho,

stopping and blowing trumpet – Josh. 6:15,16)

9. Eve (mime picking fruit from tree, eating it and offering it to Adam – Gen. 3:6)

10. Princess (mime washing, then stopping to look, pointing, opening a basket and holding a baby – Exod. 2:5,6)

For: 7's to 11's

1. Steward (mime man in charge of wine at wedding feast, tasting wine, pouring some out, calling bridegroom – John 2:8–11)

2. Jesus (mime Jesus weeping at Lazarus' tomb – John 11:35)

3. Peter (mime him walking on water, wobbling, looking frightened and falling – Matt. 14:29,30)

4. David (mime him playing his harp – I Sam. 16:23)

5. Lot's wife (mime walking along slowly, looking back and suddenly 'freezing' – Gen. 19:17,26)

6. Soldier at cross (mime him dividing out clothes, throwing dice and looking excited because he will get Jesus' garment – John 19:24)

7. Bartimaeus (mime with eyes shut and arms outstretched, then getting up, opening eyes and looking happy – Mark 10:46–52)

8. Samson (mime him entertaining guests, then putting arms round pillars, pushing and squeezing hard and collapsing – Judges 16:24,25,29,30)

9. John the Baptist (mime baptising and preaching – Mark 1:4)

10. Paul (mime him travelling, then seeing light, falling to ground, listening, then getting up and groping about – Acts 9:3–8)

For: 11's to 16's

1. Zechariah (mime him writing, then looking very happy because his speech has returned – Luke 1:63,64)

2. Belshazzar (mime him laughing and eating,

26

then suddenly looking terrified and trembling as he points to something on the wall – Dan. 5:1–6)

3. Jehoash (mime shooting arrow, then striking ground three times with other arrows – 2 Kings 13:15–19)

4. Widow woman (mime pouring oil into lots of bottles, then looking round for more containers – 2 Kings 4:4–6)

5. Peter (mime him fishing, then opening fish's mouth, finding coin and paying tax – Matt. 17:27)

6. Paul (mime him being let down from walls of Damascus in a basket – Acts 9:23–25)

7. Sarah (mime her listening at the tent door and laughing – Gen. 18:10–15)

8. Jonathan (mime shooting arrows, pointing into distance, calling – 1 Samuel 20:33–40)

9. Soldier (mime one of Gideon's army drinking water from cupped hands – Judges 7:6)

10. Simeon (mime him taking baby Jesus in his arms, looking upwards, smiling, and speaking – Luke 2:28–32)

(The above mimes can be adapted to acting.)

Guess your own Bible person

Preparation: Paper, writing implements and paper clips or safety pins.

Organization: Each child has the name of a Bible person pinned on to his back. He asks someone to mime a clue for him. If he can't guess from the first mime he asks someone else to mime for him. He must also mime for others when asked. This is a good non-competitive opening activity.

Guess all the Bible people – miming/acting relay

Preparation: Have a prepared list of people.

Organization: Divide the children into groups. One child from each group comes to the leader and is told which character to mime. He mimes this character to the group, giving only 'yes' or 'no' answers to questions. When the Bible character is guessed, someone else from the group goes to the leader for the next person to act. The group which guesses all the people on the list first wins.

For: 5's to 11's

Guess all the people — Bible statues
Preparation: Have a list of subjects for Bible statues.
Organization: Play as one group. Choose three or four children, and give each child a subject for a statue. These children march round a Bible placed in the centre of the room, while the rest sing to the tune, 'Here we go round the Mulberry Bush':

Here we march round the word of God,
The word of God, the word of God,
Here we march round the word of God,
To make a Bible statue.

On the word 'statue' the marching children 'freeze' into a Bible statue, and stay frozen until someone guesses who they are.

Repeat the game with different mimers.
Bible statue suggestions:

For: 5's to 7's

the woman looking for her lost coin (Luke 15:8)
David aiming a stone at Goliath (1 Sam. 17:49)
Joseph working as a carpenter (Matt. 13:55)
Zacchaeus climbing tree (Luke 19:4)
Jesus beckoning a disciple (Matt. 4:19)
Mary nursing baby Jesus (Luke 2:7)

For: 7's to 11's

David chopping off Goliath's head (1 Sam. 17:51)
the sower sowing his seed (Matt. 13:3,4)
Samson with arms round pillars (Judges 16:29,30)
Jesus showing Thomas his hands (John 20:27)
woman bent double (Luke 13:11)
Miriam dancing after crossing the sea (Exod. 15:20)
David playing harp (1 Sam. 16:23)
Blind Bartimaeus (Mark 10:46–52)

b. Guess a Bible event

For: 7's to 11's

Organization: Divide the children into groups and let each group decide upon a Bible event to research and mime. Each group mimes to the rest. If a mime is guessed correctly, the miming group wins a point, and so does the group guessing the mime.

Some suggestions:
1. The golden bull (Exod. 32:1–29)
2. The paralysed man who came through a roof (Luke 5:17–26)
3. Joseph put in a well and sold (Gen. 37:18–28)
4. Jacob steals Esau's blessing (Gen. 27:1–40)
5. Cain kills Abel (Gen. 4:2–8)
6. Fall of Jericho (Josh. 6:1–21)
7. Ten lepers and Jesus (Luke 17:11–19)
8. The blazing furnace (Dan. 3)
9. Paul and Silas in prison (Acts 16:16–34)
10. Peter's escape from prison (Acts 12:6–12)

Who's who?

For: 11's to 16's

Preparation: You will need a list of Bible events with three or more characters involved.

Organization: Divide the children into groups, and give each group a subject to research and prepare. One group mimes to the other groups. The guessing groups must work out who the main characters in the story are.

Some suggestions:
1. Naboth's vineyard (1 Kings 21:1–28)
2. Hannah prays for a child (1 Sam. 1)
3. Naomi's return to Bethlehem (Ruth 1:6–22; 2:1–9)
4. Three men visit Abraham (Gen. 18:1–16)
5. Jairus' daughter (Luke 8:40–42; 49–56)
6. Esther's feast (Esther 4–7)
7. Dinner at Bethany (John 12:1–8)
8. Jesus at Lake Tiberias (John 21:1–19)
9. Ananias and Sapphira (Acts 5:1–10)
10. Saul's conversion (Acts 9:1–19)

29

(With the addition of words, these mimes can be made into playlets.)

Guess all the Bible events

For: 7's to 16's

Preparation: Make a list of Bible events that can be mimed by one person.

Organization: Divide the children into groups. One child from each group goes to the leader to find out the first mime, and acts it to the rest of his group. The group which guesses all the events first, wins.

Some suggestions: (7's to 11's)
1. God calls Samuel (1 Sam. 3:1–14)
2. Jesus at the Last Supper (Matt. 26:26–29)
3. Healing of the man with paralysed hand (Matt. 12:9–13)
4. Jesus stills the storm (Matt. 8:23–27)

Some suggestions: (11's to 16's)
1. Jesus washes the disciples' feet (John 13:2–12)
2. Samson breaks ropes and uses jawbone of donkey (Judges 15:14–17)
3. David pretends to be mad (1 Sam. 21:13)
4. Moses strikes the rock (Exod. 17:5)
5. Agabus uses Paul's belt (Acts 21:10,11)

c. Mime/Act Bible themes

For: 7's to 16's

Preparation: Think of a Bible theme, e.g. Jesus' character, God speaks to people, forgiveness, Jesus the healer, Jesus the teacher, Jesus changes people, Jesus is God. Then make a list of Bible events which illustrate that theme. The children have to guess the story and then say what it teaches about the theme. It would be helpful to write up the answers and conclusions on a board.

Organization: Divide the children into groups and give each group a mime to research and prepare.

Some suggestions: What was Jesus like?
1. Jesus feeds 5,000 men (Jesus cared for

30

people's physical and spiritual needs — Mark 6:30–44)

2. The woman who touched Jesus' cloak (Jesus is stronger than disease or disability — Luke 8:43–48)

3. Jesus stills a storm (Jesus is in control of nature — Luke 8:22–25)

4. Jesus tells the story of the unforgiving servant (Jesus wants us to forgive others always, because God forgives us for so much — Matt. 18:21–35)

5. Jesus is transfigured (Jesus real glory as the Son of God — Luke 9:28–36)

d. Mime/act a modern version of a Bible theme or story

For: 11's to 16's

This is a good way of helping children to apply Bible truths to their everyday lives.

Preparation: Have a list of Bible events or stories, and some ideas of modern interpretations in case the children need help.

Organization: Divide the children into groups. Each group can be given the same story, and told to interpret it in their own way, or can choose their own stories or themes. This can be competitive or non-competitive.

Some suggestions:

1. The Pharisee and the tax-collector (Luke 18:9–14)

Characters needed: Humble person, show-off and others for the show-off to talk to.

Scene: family mealtime. One child washes up, the other refuses, then goes to bedroom, cries, prays, looks happy and goes back to the family. The child who has washed up tells everyone what he has done, then says he will have a quiet time, and reads the Bible in front of everyone.

2. The Good Samaritan (Luke 10:25–37)

Characters needed: The traveller, two people who didn't help, and the one who did. In a play version, the Samaritan could be of a different

nationality or a supporter of a rival football team.
Scene: The traveller mimes cycling along. He falls
off his bike. Two people come along and either
take no notice or actually grab and run off with his
bike. A third person comes along, retrieves the
bike and takes the boy home.

3. Workers in the vineyard (Matt. 20:1–16)
Characters needed: Grandad and several
children.
Scene: Grandad holds up twenty pence, saying
that he will give that amount to any of the
children who will do his gardening. Some start at
once. Others start later. When they each get
twenty pence, those who have worked longer
grumble and point at the others.

4. Two sons (Matt. 21:28–32)
Characters needed: Mum and two children.
Scene: Mum asks two children to do a job. One
agrees but does nothing. The other refuses then
later changes his mind and does the job.

5. The widow's mite (Luke 21:1–4)
Characters needed: Rich person, poor person,
people in the congregation.
Scene: Church collection is being taken. Rich
person ostentatiously pulls out wallet stuffed
with notes. He puts in £1. The other person
secretly empties total contents of purse into
collection, about 30p.

7. Tenants in the vineyard (Matt. 21:33–45)
Characters needed: Business owner, two or three employees, son and about three contractors in charge of business.
Scene: Owner keeps sending employees to receive profits. Instead of handing over the profits, the contractors attack the employees. Then he sends his son. The contractors kill him.

8. Lost coin (Luke 15:8–10)
Characters needed: Old woman and neighbours.
Scene: Old woman is very upset at losing her wedding ring. When she finds it, she asks her neighbours in to have a celebratory tea with her!

9. Unforgiving servant (Matt. 18:21–35)
Characters needed: Father and two children.
Scene: Father calls in elder child and asks where the £1 is that he lent him. Child mimes or says that he has spent it and is very upset. Father lets him off. This child then goes and asks younger brother where the 2p which he lent him is. The young brother has lost it and is upset. The brother beats him up. Father sees and is furious.

6. QUIZ IDEA

LIST-FILLING QUIZZES

Children can complete the lists — competing in teams or working individually or together. You can devise questions about Bible names, people, places or books.

Age Group: Seniors

Examples: **a. Alphabetical listing**
Organization: On the left hand side of paper or board you or the children write as many categories as you can think of, e.g. man, woman, book, town, mountain. On the right-hand side the children write down the name of something, someone or some place that fits in each category, each beginning with one (previously chosen) letter of the alphabet.

Example, listing with the letter 'j':

Man   Jesse
Woman   Jael
King   Jehoshaphat
River   Jordan
Country   Judah
Miracle   Jairus' daughter.

If the children are competing, award points to those whose lists are longest and/or contain the most unusual words and names.

b. Listing Bible books
Organization: Divide the children into teams and set a time limit. In the left-hand column write the categories, leaving enough space for the children to fill in the names of the Bible books. See which team can fill in the most names in the given time.
Categories:
Old Testament history (17 books)
Old Testament poetry (2 books)
Old Testament prophecy (17 books)
New Testament Gospels and history (5 books)
New Testament letters (21 books)
New Testament prophecy (1 book).

c. Listing the 'I am' sayings of Jesus

d. Listing Jesus' miracles and/or parables

e. Listing Jesus' statements beginning 'Happy are . . .'

f. Listing Jesus' statements about life and death.

7. QUIZ IDEA
LISTEN AND TELL QUIZZES

These are verbal or written puzzles in which children compete in teams or work together. The quizzes can be used either to introduce new material, or to revise previous lessons.

A story is prepared which gives a lot of factual information, and is told to the children. It is then given again, with gaps, wrong words, mixed up words or a number of different words in place of the correct word.

Age Groups: Primaries, Juniors

Examples:

For: 5's to 7's

a. Bible background – a day in the life of a Jewish family

Preparation: You may need to consult some of the Bible background books listed in the Sources section on page 94. Make up and write out one copy of a story about a day in the life of a Jewish family in Bible times. In your story mention that in the children's home there were no knives, forks and spoons, no chairs, no beds (as we know them), no window panes and no taps (for water). Talk about sitting on the floor, eating with fingers, going to the well, rolling up sleeping mattresses or mats, lighting the lamp. Draw an enlarged copy of some of the words and pictures.

Organization: Work together. After the story, let the children tell you the missing words.

In Ruth's and Dan's home there were no...

K_____ , f_____ or s_____
ch_____
b_____
w_____ p_____
t_____

For: 7's to 11's

b. Bible background – the wheat harvest

Preparation: Make up and write out one copy of a story about harvest time on a wheat farm in Bible times. Make the story as exciting as possible. For

35

instance, you could have the threat of a swarm of locusts. In your story you could include: the wheat was cut, trodden or threshed, winnowed, stored, ground.

Make a large copy of the words and pictures and have suitable writing implements.

Organization: Work as a group, letting children volunteer, after the story, to come and write in the missing letters.

At harvest time the wheat was...
c _ _
t _ _ _ _ _ _ _ or th _ _ _ _ _ _
w _ _ _ _ _ _ _ _
s _ _ _ _ _
g _ _ _ _ _

Locust   ploughing   winnowing

8. QUIZ IDEA

MAP QUIZZES

These are written and drawn quizzes, suitable for children competing in teams or working individually or together. You can devise them about Bible places and the people and events connected with them.

Age Groups: Juniors, Seniors

Examples: a. **Mixed-up place names**

Preparation: You will need large maps of Bible lands with dots marking important places, but no names. Write the names on pieces of card and stick each by the wrong dot (using Blu-Tack).

Organization: See whether the children can put the place names in the correct positions. If you want to make this a competitive quiz, have two maps with the same number of place-names and see which team is the first to re-arrange their place-names correctly.

(See page 94 for map sources.)

b. What's this place? (with clues)

Preparation: Have large maps, cards with place names, and Blu-Tack. Have a list of clues about each of the place names.

Organization: Point to a red dot and ask, 'What's this place?' Give clues until the name is guessed. The child who guesses, attaches the name to the map.

Some suggestions:

Its walls fell down. (Joshua 6:20)

Jesus healed two blind men after leaving it. (Matt. 20:29)

The traveller going from Jerusalem to this place was robbed. (Luke 10:30)

All the letters in it, except one, are also in the word 'rejoice'.

(Answer: Jericho)

c. What's this place?(with Bible verses)

Preparation: Have a map of the area you wish to concentrate on with the place names numbered only, a list of Bible references about each place, and a Bible for each child.

Organization: The children look up the Bible passages to find out the names.

Suggestion:

Jonah's travels: God told Jonah to go to . . . (Jonah 1:2) but instead he went to . . . (Jonah 1:3). (Nineveh, Joppa).

9. QUIZ IDEA

MEMORY VERSE QUIZZES

Make sure the verses you choose are important, intelligible and memorable.

Age Groups: Primaries, Juniors, Seniors

Examples: **a. Say a word each**

Organization: Children sit in a circle and say one word each, in sequence, of the memory verse. Those who cannot contribute a word shake their heads or quietly say 'pass'. Continue saying the verse more and more smoothly and quickly until it 'flows' and makes sense. Children who shook their heads and passed, can join in again whenever they are able to.

b. Rub off a word (reading invisible writing)

Preparation: Write a verse on paper, board or acetate sheet for overhead projector.

Organization: Ask the group to read the verse together several times. Rub off one word and ask the group to read the 'invisible' word when they say the verse again. Continue this way until all the words are rubbed off, but children can still say the words.

As an alternative: write out the verse using different colours for the words. A child chooses a colour and the words in that colour are rubbed off.

Or: write out the words of the verse on pieces of card (one word per card) and attach the cards to a board with Blu-Tack. Turn the cards round one at a time so that the blank side is showing.

c. Re-arrange the words

Write out the words on pieces of card and attach them to the board in an incorrect order. Let the children re-arrange the cards to make the verse.

d. Burst a balloon

Preparation: Using sticky paper or ordinary paper and sellotape, attach the words of the verse on to balloons. Children hold up the balloons so that the verse is spelt out correctly. The balloons are burst one at a time as the verse is repeated until all the balloons are burst, and the verse has been learnt.

10. QUIZ IDEA

MIXED-UP STORY QUIZZES

Age Group: Seniors

Examples: a. **The Lost Sheep** (Luke 15:4–7)

The Prodigal Son (Luke 15:11–32)

The Good Samaritan (Luke 10:25–32)

Preparation: Choose three readers and give each a copy of the mixed-up story. Let them practise reading together.

Organization: Ask the children to listen hard and afterwards tell you the three confused stories, and perhaps which reader was 'telling' each of them.

Examples:

Reader 1: There's a story in the Bible about
Reader 2: a shepherd who
Reader 3: decided to leave home.
Reader 1: As he went along the road he was attacked by
Reader 2: a hundred sheep who
Reader 3: spent all his money.
Reader 1: The robbers went away
Reader 2: and got lost.
Reader 3: in the big city.
Reader 1: A religious man
Reader 2: left the ninety-nine sheep and
Reader 3: felt very hungry after a time
Reader 1: but he didn't stop
Reader 2: to look for the lost
Reader 3: pig's food.
Reader 1: Another religious man
Reader 2: found the lost one
Reader 3: hungry and sorry and
Reader 1: he stopped to help
Reader 2: and took him back to the sheepfold
Reader 3: and went home to his father.

b. Daniel and the king's food (Dan. 1:6–21)

Jonah (Jonah 1–4)

Moses at the palace (Exod. 2:1–14)

Reader 1: I'm going to tell you
Reader 2: to go and preach to
Reader 3: Amram and Jochabed.
Reader 1: These Jews were captured and taken to
Reader 2: a seaport called Joppa where
Reader 3: a baby son was born
Reader 1: hundreds of miles from home
Reader 2: on a boat to Tarshish.
Reader 3: He could no longer be hidden so
Reader 1: the king chose the best young men to be
Reader 2: terrified by a sudden storm
Reader 3: hidden in a basket and
Reader 1: fed with specially-prepared rich food
Reader 2: while praying to their gods.
Reader 3: His sister watched while
Reader 1: the men refused to eat
Reader 2: an enormous fish
Reader 3: and the princess and her maidens
Reader 1: asked for plain food instead.
Reader 2: Three days were spent
Reader 3: bathing in the river.
Reader 1: After ten days the officer
Reader 2: spat him out on dry land
Reader 3: and took him to the palace where
Reader 1: they looked better and healthier than
Reader 2: the men of Nineveh who listened to
Reader 3: an Egyptian prince.
Reader 1: So they were allowed to go on
Reader 2: repenting of their sins and
Reader 3: felt sad that the Israelites
Reader 1: pleased the king of Babylon but their
Reader 2: changed way of life so
Reader 3: he killed an Egyptian and ran away to the desert.

11. QUIZ IDEA

MUSICAL QUIZZES

Audio-verbal quizzes for children competing in teams, or working individually or together.

You can devise them about songs or music based on Bible themes.

See page 95 for suggested sources of music.

Age Groups: Primaries, Juniors, Seniors

Examples:

For: 5's to 16's

a. Guess the song

Organization: Play a few bars of a well-known carol, hymn, song or chorus and let the children tell you the first line or title.

For: 5's to 7's

b. Link song and picture

Preparation: Make enlarged copies of the pictures below on ten pieces of card or on a large sheet of paper or on an acetate sheet for overhead projector. Attach cards to board with Blu-Tack. Tape record a few bars of each of the songs. Alternatively be prepared to hum a few bars yourself.

Organization: Work as a group. Play a few bars of the first song and let a child hold up or point to the picture that links with it. Give the first line of the song and talk with the children about the connection between song and picture.

Some suggestions:

1. Now Zacchaeus was a very little man
2. While shepherds watched
3. All things bright and beautiful
4. We plough the fields and scatter
5. There is a green hill
6. Only a boy named David
7. Thank you for the world so sweet
8. Jesus loves me, this I know
9. How did Moses cross the Red Sea?
10. Away in a manger.

c. Sing the rest

For: 7's to 16's

> *Organization:* Play two or three lines of a well-known carol, hymn, song or chorus, and ask the children to sing the rest. If you are playing competitively, you could award one point for humming the rest of the tune and two for singing the words.

12. QUIZ IDEA

PICTURE RELAY QUIZZES

Drawing quizzes for children competing in teams. You can devise them about Bible background, events, objects or animals.

Age Groups: Juniors, Seniors

> *Preparation:* Have papers and pencils and a numbered list of the events you want the children to draw.
>
> *Organization:* Divide the children into teams. Let one child from each team come to you for the first subject. He draws this for the rest of the group, but cannot speak, only nodding or shaking his head in answer to questions. The child who guesses the subject comes to you for the next subject. The team who completes the list first is the winning team.
>
> Include events you wish to revise.
>
> *The following are possible subjects:*
> Jonah being swallowed by the whale
> Noah building an Ark
> The flood
> Moses and the Ten Commandments
> Moses hitting the rock
> Elijah pouring water over his sacrifice
> Peter walking on the water to Jesus
> The big catch of fish
> Peter finding a coin in the fish's mouth
> Jesus washing the disciples' feet
> Palm Sunday
> Mary pouring perfume on Jesus' feet

Paul and Silas singing in prison
Jesus being baptised by John
The Israelites crossing the sea
Jesus walking on water to the disciples' boat.

13. QUIZ IDEA

QUESTION QUIZZES

Written or verbal quizzes for children competing in teams or working individually or together.

You can devise them about Bible background, books, events, objects, animals, people, places, themes, or verses. It is better to cover one event, one book or one theme.

How to ask questions

1. Have a numbered list of questions and either write them up or read them out in the right order to the group.

2. Instead of directing questions to everyone, direct them to alternate teams or different age groups — and grade the questions accordingly.

3. As an alternative to the leader choosing the question for the child, let the children choose a question number.

4. Prepare questions on a number of themes, and let the children choose the theme on which they are prepared to be questioned. (Themes might be: Bible books, Paul, Jesus, or another Bible person, Bible people (in general), the parables, the miracles or Bible events).

Where to put the questions

1. Write them on a leader's list.

2. Write them on paper, board or acetate sheet for an overhead projector.

   (Some children cope with written questions much better than verbal ones, and some questions, especially those which require thought, need to be written out.)

3. Duplicate them on to pieces of paper, one for each child, pair of children or small group.

4. Hide them in balloons. This is fun for small

groups of older primaries or juniors. You need as many balloons as questions, paper cut in thin strips with the questions written on them, string and a pin. Push the strips of paper into the balloons before blowing and tying them up. Children take turns to prick a balloon and answer the question which falls out.

5. Pin them to fish. Small groups of primaries enjoy this method. You need thin coloured card, paper, pins or paper clips, scissors, a stick, string, magnet and plastic bucket. Write the questions on bits of paper and attach them to the fish shapes (cut out of card) with pins or paper clips. Put these in the bucket. Make a magnetic rod by tying the magnet to one end of the string and the rod to the other. Children fish for questions. Answers could be fished for in the same way, and these could be pictures.

6. Pin them to people's backs. Juniors or seniors could cope with this idea. You need a numbered question for each person, paper, pencils and safety pins. Each person goes round writing down answers to the question on everyone's back except his own.

7. Attach them to the walls.

8. Hide them round the room. Each child needs paper and pencil. He goes round finding, answering and replacing questions. Alternatively, give each child a different question to find and answer.

What questions to ask
a. Questions beginning with 'Who?'
(i) Who am I?
Leader pretends to be a Bible person and talks about himself, giving titbits of information until the character is guessed.

(ii) Who am I? (rhyming clues)
Make up humorous, relevant rhyming couplets about the people.

(iii) Who said it?
Quote or paraphrase the words of Bible people and ask the children to identify each speaker.
Suggestion: The raising of Lazarus (John 11)
1. Who said, 'Let us all go with the teacher, so that we may die with him'? (Thomas — verse 16)
2. Who said, 'I know that he will rise to life'? (Martha — verse 24)
3. Who said, 'If you had been here, my brother would not have died'? (Martha, Mary — v.21,32)
4. Who said, 'See how much he loved him'? (the people — verse 36)
5. Who said, 'I am the resurrection and the life'? (Jesus — verse 25)
6. Who said, 'If he is asleep, Lord, he will get well'? (the disciples — verse 12)
7. Who said, 'Lazarus, come out'? (Jesus — verse 43)
8. Who said, 'Could he not have kept Lazarus from dying'? (the people — verse 37)
9. Who said, 'There will be a bad smell, Lord. He has been buried four days'? (Martha — verse 39)
10. Who said, 'This has happened in order to bring glory to God'? (Jesus — verse 4)

(iv) Who might have said it.
Preparation: Make up sentences or phrases Bible people might well have said or thought and ask children to identify the likely or possible speakers.
Organization: Divide the children into teams. You could award two points if Bibles are not used, and one if they are.

Some suggestions:

For: 5's to 7's

1. 'That giant's dead! And I didn't need your armour.' (David – 1 Sam. 17:50)
2. 'What does the fruit taste like, Eve? I think I'll try some, too.' (Adam – Gen. 3:6)
3. 'Come on, let's leave the sheep and hurry to see the baby.' (the shepherds – Luke 2:15)
4. 'Look what I've found in a floating basket – a lovely baby!' (the princess – Exod. 2:5,6)
5. 'These lions aren't going to have me for supper, after all!' (Daniel – Dan. 6:22)

For: 7's to 11's

1. 'No, I haven't drowned . . . I've been swallowed.' (Jonah – Jonah 1:17)
2. 'I took five coins from you, please take twenty coins from me, I'm a changed man now.' (Zacchaeus – Luke 19:1–9)
3. 'Quick, where's my harp? I don't like the look on King Saul's face.' (David – 1 Sam. 16:23)
4. 'Goodbye, Dad, James and I are going with Jesus now.' (John – Matt. 4:22)
5. 'I wash my hands but I cannot wash away the memory of that prisoner who spoke so calmly.' (Pilate – Matt. 27:24)

For: 11's to 16's

1. 'Fancy my donkey seeing an angel before I did!' (Balaam – Numb. 22:31–33)
2. 'Peter, John and I became really frightened when our master became white and dazzling.' (James – Mark 9:2)
3. 'Listen wife, we'll pretend we only got this much money for the property.' (Ananias – Acts 5:2)
4. 'I think I'll go back to my family after all – Bethlehem is a long way from home.' (Orpah – Ruth 1:14)
5. 'It's Peter who's standing outside knocking!' (Rhoda – Acts 12:12–14)

b. Questions beginning with 'Where?'

Ask the children questions about places and the events connected with them.

Organization: One approach would be to write the question numbers down one side of the paper, board or acetate sheet, and the places on the other side, in the wrong order. Children could draw lines linking the numbers and answers, preferably using different colours.

(i) Where was Jesus?

For: 5's to 7's

Preparation: Make an enlarged copy of the pictures below.

1. Where was Jesus born?

2. Where was Jesus brought up?

3. Where did Jesus go to sleep in a storm?

4. Where was Jesus when people waved palm branches?

5. Where did Jesus die?

6. Where is Jesus now?

ANSWERS: (i) 1. In a manger in Bethlehem; 2. In a house in Nazareth; 3. In a boat on Lake Galilee; 4. On a donkey going to Jerusalem; 6. With God in heaven.

Organization: Read out each question and talk about the picture before asking for an answer. Work as one group or compete in teams.

If you wish, you can have the jumbled answers written up somewhere to help the children, or have up picture clues.

For: 7's to 11's

1. Where was Jesus born? (Bethlehem – Matt. 2:1)
2. Where was he taken as a baby to escape from Herod? (Egypt – Matt. 2:14,15)
3. Where was Jesus baptised by John? (River Jordan – Matt. 3:13)
5. Where did Jesus first see Simon Peter and Andrew? (by Lake Galilee – Matt. 4:18)
6. Where did Jesus ride on a donkey surrounded by shouting crowds? (Jerusalem – Matt. 21:6–10)
7. Where was Jesus praying while his friends slept? (Gethsemane – Matt. 26:36,39,40)
8. Where was Jesus crucified? (Golgotha – Matt. 27:33)
9. Where did the eleven disciples see Jesus after he had risen from the dead? (Galilee – Matt. 28:16)
10. Where did Jesus live most of his life? (Palestine)

(iii) Places visited by Paul

For: 7's to 16's

Organization: Divide the children into competing teams, and give each team paper and pencil for working out and writing down the answers.

1. Where were Paul and Silas put in prison for healing a slave girl? PPPIIILH (Philippi – Acts 16:24)
2. Where did Paul see an altar to an unknown god and preach a sermon to a city council? TSNEAH (Athens – Acts 17:16–33)

3. Where did Paul preach a long sermon to a king and queen? SCAAAREE (Caesarea — Acts 25:13,26)
4. Where did Paul and others land after the shipwreck? AATLM (Malta — Acts 28:1)
5. Where did Paul await trial by the Emperor? MROE (Rome — Acts 28:16)
6. Where was Paul going when he became a Christian? SCAAMDUS (Damascus — Acts 9:2,4)
7. Where did forty Jews vow not to eat until they had killed Paul? SUEERMAJL (Jerusalem — Acts 23:11–13)
8. Where was a silversmith furious because Paul spoke against man-made gods? SEESUPH (Ephesus — Acts 19:26)
9. Where did Paul make tents with Priscilla and Aquila? TRINCHO (Corinth — Acts 18:1–3)
10. Where did people try to make a sacrifice to Paul and Barnabas? RALSTY (Lystra — Acts 14:8,11–13)

c. Questions beginning with 'Which?' or 'What?'

(i) What was the relationship between x and y?
Example: Abraham and Lot (uncle and nephew — Gen. 12:5)

(ii) What is this picture about?

a. Picture of a Bible event
Preparation: You will need good, detailed, accurate pictures, large enough for your group. Devise questions which the children can answer by studying and thinking about the picture. With older children you could also include questions about what preceded or followed the event portrayed. (See page 94 for picture sources.)

b. Picture-strip story of Bible events and people
Buy or make your own picture-strip stories and base your questions on these. (See page 95 for picture-strip sources.)

c. Guess what I'm drawing
You need an artist who will draw boldly and

quickly a Bible object, scene, person, place or event in such a way that the children will be kept guessing for a while.

(iii) What did they say?

Preparation: Think of important things said by Bible people and devise a quiz about them suited to your age group. In some cases, it would be helpful to have the speeches written up.

For: 5's to 7's

1. What did Jesus say to Mary when she was crying in the garden? (John 20:16)
2. What did the angel tell Joseph to call Mary's baby? (Matt. 1:21)
3. What did God tell Moses to do near the holy ground by the burning bush? (Exod. 3:5)
4. What was one of the commands that God gave to Moses on the mountain? (Exod. 20:1–17)
5. What did the people shout when Jesus rode into Jerusalem on a donkey? (Matt. 21:9)
6. What did Peter say three times when Jesus was being tried before he died? (Matt. 26:74)
7. What did Jesus say when the disciples wanted to send the children away? (Mark 10:14)
8. What did the angels tell the shepherds they would find in Bethlehem? (Luke 2:12)
9. What did Jesus say to Jairus' daughter when he brought her back to life? (Mark 5:41)
10. What did Jesus say when he saw Peter and Andrew by Lake Galilee? (Matt. 4:19)

For: 7's to 11's

1. After the earthquake what did the jailer say to Paul and Silas? (Acts 16:30)
2. What did John the Baptist say when Jesus came to be baptised? (Matt. 3:14)
4. What did Paul say when he fell to the ground on the way to Damascus? (Acts 9:5)
5. What did the people say when Elijah called down fire from heaven? (1 Kings 18:39)
6. What did Jesus' mother say to the servants at the wedding in Cana? (John 2:5)

7. What did Jesus ask Peter three times on the sea shore? (John 21:17)
8. What did God say when Jesus was baptised? (Matt. 3:17)
9. What did Shadrach, Meshach and Abednego say to King Nebuchadnezzar before they were put in the blazing furnace? (Dan. 3:17,18)
10. What did Jesus say when his parents found him in the Temple when he was twelve? (Luke 2:49)

For: 11's to 16's

1. What did Peter say when Jesus asked his disciples who they thought he was? (Matt. 16:16)
2. What were the angel's first words to Gideon? (Judges 6:12)
3. What did Jesus say when the Pharisees tried to trap him about paying taxes? (Luke 20:25)
4. What did Esther say to Mordecai when she decided she would go to the king? (Esther 4:16)
5. What did King Agrippa say after hearing Paul's defence? (Acts 26:28)
6. What did Jeremiah say when God called him to be a prophet? (Jer. 1:6)
7. What did the lepers say when they found the Syrian camp deserted after the siege of Samaria? (2 Kings 7:9)
8. What did John the Baptist tell the people to do? (Luke 3:3)
9. What did John the Baptist say when he pointed out Jesus? (John 1:29)
10. What did Peter say to the man at the Beautiful Gate of the Temple? (Acts 3:6)

(iv) Which commandment is being kept/broken? Draw pictures of situations in which any of the Ten Commandments is being kept or broken. Bibles should be available, or the Ten Commandments should be written up.
Organization: Work together. Ask children to volunteer to come and write by each picture the number of the commandment and either 'kept' or

'broken' beside it.

(Alternatively, these situations could be mimed for a guessing game.)

(v) Which book?

Preparation: Prepare questions beginning, 'In which book do we read of . . . ?' Questions could be on a theme such as prisons and punishment or *Suggested illustrations for 7's to 16's*

ANSWERS: (iv) A. 5 broken; B. 10 broken; C. 9 kept; D. 4 kept; E. 8 broken; F. 1 kept.

kings and queens.

For Seniors you could range over several Bible books. For Juniors, keep to fewer books, which you have already looked at with them.

For: 7's to 11's

Which book? (Genesis/Esther/Gospels/Acts)

Preparation: Have four large pieces of paper or card with one each of the following written on them: The Gospels, Genesis, Acts, Esther. Have a copy of the questions and answers.

Organization: Divide the children into two teams. Prop up the four pieces of card. As soon as a child answers a question correctly, he can come and hold up the appropriate card. When someone else guesses the same book he has to hand it over to that person. If at any time all four pieces of card are held up by members of the same team, that team wins.

1. In which book or books do we read of a queen giving a party for a king? (Esther)

2. In which book or books do we read that Jesus helped to create the world? (the Gospels)

3. In which book or books do we read of a man giving a party to which none of the invited guests came? (the Gospels)

4. In which book or books do we read of people being healed through Jesus' power? (Acts and the Gospels)

5. In which book or books do we read of Jesus being baptised? (the Gospels)

6. In which book or books do we read the story of Abraham? (Genesis)

7. In which book or books do we find the story of an important man who was hanged on his own gallows? (Esther)

8. In which book or books do we find people put into prison for doing right? (Genesis, the Gospels, Acts)

9. In which book or books do we read of the first rainbow? (Genesis)

10. In which book or books do we read of a man who went blind for a few days after meeting Jesus on a journey? (Acts)

For: 11's to 16's

(vi) Which book? (Exodus, Daniel, John, Acts)
1. In which book did Jesus wash some people's feet? (John)
2. In which book did the Israelites leave Egypt? (Exodus)
3. In which book are 5000 people fed? (John)
4. In which book did some men choose to drink water instead of wine? (Daniel)
5. In which book did Jesus change water into wine? (John)
6. Which book comes after Ezekiel? (Daniel)
7. In which book was a lame man healed outside a Temple gate? (Acts)
8. In which book does a woman wash Jesus' feet? (John)
9. In which book did people burn their magic books? (Acts)
10. In which book do some men choose to eat vegetables instead of rich food? (Daniel)
11. In which book do people find food on the ground morning and evening? (Exodus)
12. In which book was clay used to heal a blind man? (John)
13. In which book do we find lots of people becoming Christians on the same day? (Acts)
14. In which book does a princess adopt a baby? (Exodus)
15. In which book did someone claim to be the light of the world? (John)

(viii) Which chapter and book?
Preparation: Prepare some well-known words from a well-known Bible passage. These can be written out on a large card, or duplicated copies can be prepared.
Organization: Working individually or in teams ask the children to tell you the book and chapter

55

from which the passages are taken.
Some suggestions:
1. 'The Lord is my shepherd.' (Psalm 23:1)
2. 'In the beginning when God created the universe, the earth was formless and desolate.' (Genesis 1:1,2)
3. 'Before the world was created, the Word already existed.' (John 1:1)
4. 'When the day of Pentecost came, all the believers were gathered together in one place.' (Acts 2:1)
5. 'There is no condemnation now for those who live in union with Christ Jesus.' (Romans 8:1)
6. 'To have faith is to be sure of the things we hope for.' (Hebrews 11:1)
7. 'Then I saw a new heaven and a new earth.' (Revelation 21:1)
8. 'The Lord is my light and my salvation.' (Psalm 27:1)
9. 'I am the real vine, and my Father is the gardener.' (John 15:1)
10. 'In the past, God spoke to our ancestors many times and in many ways through the prophets.' (Hebrews 1:1)

d. Questions beginning with 'How?'
Verbal quizzes with all the questions beginning with 'How?' This can lead to children searching their Bibles for answers or thinking deeply about Bible events. The questions can lead to discussion about the answers.

For: 11's to 16's
1. How often should we forgive each other? (Matt. 18:21,22)
2. How do we know God loves us? (1 John 4:9,10 and other verses)
3. How much does God love us? (John 3:16)
4. How can we show our love for God? (1 John 3:16—18 and other verses)
5. How should we treat our parents? (Eph. 6:1—3)

56

6. How should we treat people who persecute us? (Matt. 5:44)
7. How far away does God take our sins when he forgives us? (Psalm 103:12)
8. How should we do our work? (Col. 3:23)
9. How soon will Jesus return? (Mark 13:32)
10. How should we deal with the Devil? (James 4:7)

How Many?

For: 5's to 16's

Preparation: Devise questions about Bible numbers. Make sure that the numbers are significant.

Organization: Children can answer in many different ways:

a. In written number quizzes they can show a number, show a number-card or link numbers and questions.

b. For verbal number quizzes they can clap, jump, stand up, sit down, nod, call out or sound out the answers.

Some suggestions:

For: 5's to 7's

Questions from Jesus' life

1. How many sheep did the good shepherd go to look for? (1 – Luke 15:4)
2. How many coins did the woman have before she lost one? (10 – Luke 15:8)
3. How many fish fed 5000 people? (2 – John 6:8)
4. How many special friends did Jesus choose? (12 – Luke 6:13)
5. How many lepers did Jesus heal at the same time? (10 – Luke 17:12)
6. How many of those lepers came back to say, 'Thank you'? (1 – Luke 17:15)
7. How many others died on the hill near Jesus on Good Friday? (2 – John 19:18)
8. How many times did Peter say he didn't even know Jesus? (3 – John 18:15–27)

57

9. How many days before Jesus rose again after he had died? (3 — Mark 10:34)

10. How many of Jesus' special friends joined Jesus' enemies and betrayed Jesus? (1 — Acts 1:16,17)

For: 7's to 11's

Preparation: Cut out twelve number cards and write numbers 1 to 12 on them; do the same thing with another twelve number cards. Have a copy of the questions, answers and references.

Organization: Divide the children into two teams and give each a set of number cards. Whoever holds up the correct number card first wins a point.

1. How many loaves were used in the feeding of the 4000? (7 — Matt. 15:34)

2. How many Commandments were given to Moses on Mount Sinai? (10 — Exod. 20:1–17)

3. How many days had Lazarus been dead before Jesus brought him back to life? (4 — John 11:39)

4. How many brothers did Joseph have? (11 — Gen. 42:3,4)

5. How many sons did Sarah have? (1 — Gen. 21:1,2)

6. How many baskets were filled with what was left over after feeding the 5000? (12 — Luke 9:17)

7. How many sons did Noah have? (3 — Gen. 6:9)

8. How many Gospels are there? (4)

9. How many disciples saw Jesus bring Jairus' daughter back to life? (3 — Luke 8:51)

10. How many times as much did Zacchaeus pay back the people he had cheated? (4 — Luke 19:8)

Sound out the answer

Preparation: You will need some whistles or musical instruments capable of being struck, played, blown or rung the required number of times. Keep the answer numbers low.

Organization: Divide the children into two teams, and give each team a musical instrument. Let the children take it in turns to sound out the answer.

e. Questions beginning with 'When?'

(i) When did these events happen?
The answers to these questions will not be dates. You can ask the children to say when something happened in relation to something else.

For: 7's to 11's

Preparation: Have a copy of the questions, answers and references.

Organization: Divide the children into teams or work as one group.

1. When did Daniel pray?
    1 — every hour
    2 — three times a day
    3 — once a week
    (2 — Dan. 6:10)

2. When did Abraham have a son called Isaac?
    1 — when he was a hundred
    2 — when he was fifty
    3 — when he was ninety
    (1 — Gen. 21:5)

3. When did Moses smash the Ten Commandments?
    1 — when a wave of the Red Sea knocked them from his hand
    2 — when he was thirsty
    3 — when he saw the gold bull
    (3 — Exod. 32:19)

4. When did Esau cry?
    1 — when he married Judith
    2 — when Jacob left home
    3 — when he was re-united with Jacob
    (3 — Gen. 33:4)

5. When did Matthew stop being a tax-collector?
    1 — when Jesus said, 'Follow me.'
    2 — when he got a job as a shepherd
    3 — when he was rich enough to retire
    (1 — Matt. 9:9)

6. When did Jesus say, 'Forgive them, Father! They don't know what they are doing.'?
  1 – when the disciples went to sleep
  2 – when he was on the cross
  3 – when the crowd shouted, 'Crucify him!'
  (2 – Luke 23:33,34)

7. When did Joseph of Arimathea ask for Jesus' body?
  1 – when Jesus was on trial
  2 – when Jesus had risen again
  3 – when Jesus had died
  (3 – Luke 23:50–52)

8. When did Nicodemus visit Jesus?
  1 – at night
  2 – when Jesus was a baby
  3 – when Jesus was at Martha's house
  (1 – John 3:1,2)

9. When was Jesus mistaken for a gardener?
  1 – when he was praying in the garden of Gethsemane
  2 – when Mary was crying in the garden after Jesus had risen
  3 – when he was gardening for the widow of Nain?
  (2 – John 20:15,16)

10. When was David anointed King of Israel?
  1 – when he was a shepherd boy
  2 – when he killed Goliath
  3 – when he played the harp for Saul
  (1 – 1 Sam. 16:11–13)

For: 11's to 16's

(ii) 'When?' question quiz with Sword Drill

Preparation: You will need a copy of the questions, answers and references. The children will need the same version of the Bible.

Organization: Organize the looking up of the references as for Sword Drill (see page 87) but let each question lead into a discussion rather than a snappy answer.

1. When did Jesus come into being? (He has

always existed — John 1:1)
2. When will there be no more pain? (In heaven —
Rev. 21:4)
3. When is the time to be saved? (Now — 2 Cor.
6:2)
4. When will Christians become like Christ? (At
his Second Coming — 1 John 3:2)
5. When will Jesus come again? (We don't know
— Matt. 24:42)
6. When do we receive eternal life? (When we
receive Jesus — 1 John 5:12)
7. When should we praise God? (Always — Ps.
34:1)
8. When will God forgive our sins? (When we
confess them — 1 John 1:9)

f. Questions beginning with 'Why?'

These can stimulate thought on the reasons for or
the meaning underlying Biblical events.

For: 5's to 7's

Preparation: Make enlarged copies of the words
and pictures below.

Suggested answers:

A. To see the baby Jesus — Luke 2:15,16
B. Because King Herod wanted to kill Jesus —
Matt. 2:13
C. Because she knew Jesus would make her
better — Mark 5:28
D. To hide him from the king — Exod. 1:22,23
E. Because lots of rain was coming — Gen.
6:17–20
F. Because her sister had left her to do all the
work — Luke 10:40
G. Because Jesus said, 'Come with me' — Matt.
4:18,19
H. To get him to Jesus who would heal him —
Mark 2:4

For: 11's to 16's

'Why' quiz on Gideon. (Judges 6 to 7)

1. Why did God allow the Israelites to be ruled

61

by the Midianites? (Because they had sinned —
6:1)
2. Why was Gideon threshing wheat secretly?
(So that the Midianites wouldn't see him and
destroy or take the crop — 6:3,11)
3. Finish Gideon's words to the angel: 'If I may
ask, sir, why ... ?' (... has all this happened to us if
the Lord is with us?' — 6:13)
4. Why did Gideon question the Lord's
command to rescue the Israelites? (He said his
clan was weak and he was unimportant — 6:15)
5. Why did Gideon give the angel food?
(Because he wanted proof that this really was the
angel of the Lord — 6:17)
6. Why did Gideon tear down Baal's altar at
night? (Because he was afraid of his family and
the people — 6:27)
7. Why was Gideon known as Jerubbaal?
(Because it meant 'Let Baal defend himself'.
Because Gideon had torn down Baal's altar —
6:31,32)
8. Why did Gideon put wool on the threshing
floor at night? (To find out whether God was
going to use him to rescue Israel — 6:36,37)
9. Why did Gideon take the men to the water?
(To separate the lappers from the kneelers and so
reduce the size of his army — 7:4,5)
10. Why did Gideon only want a small army? (So
that the glory for their victory would go to God —
7:2)

For: 11's to 16's
Why did they happen?
Organization: Let the children have Bibles so that
they can look up each reference and try to
express what is said in their own words. Work
together as a group, discussing the answers.
1. Why did Jesus perform miracles? (John 2:11)
2. Why did Jesus die? (1 Pet. 3:18 and other
passages)
3. Why did Jesus come to earth? (1 John 3:8

and other passages)
4. Why was Jesus baptized? (Matt. 3:15)
5. Why did Jesus wash the disciples' feet? (John 13:15,16)
6. Why did Jesus stay where he was when he heard that Lazarus was ill? (John 11:15)

g. Mixed question quizzes, concentrating on one Bible theme, passage or event.

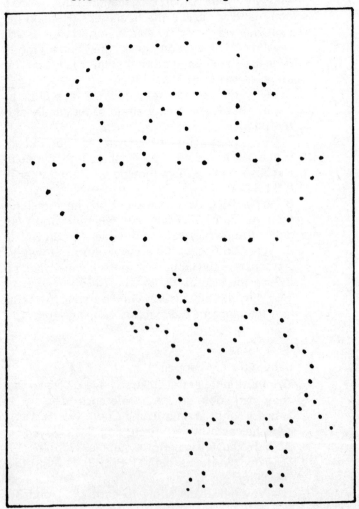

For: 7's to 11's

(i) Bible Creatures

Preparation: Have a copy of the questions, answers and references. Draw, in dot-to-dot form, using at least ten dots, the outline of Noah's Ark, a camel or any other animal, on a large sheet of card, or board.

Organization: Work as a group or compete in teams. A child who answers correctly can join up any two dots.

1. Which creatures first plagued the Egyptians when Moses was asking Pharaoh to let the Israelites go? (frogs — Exod. 8:1–15)

2. Which animal did Aaron make a golden image of for the Israelites to worship? (bull — Exod. 32:1–4)

3. Which birds brought Elijah bread and meat, morning and evening, during a famine? (ravens — 1 Kings 17:1–5)

4. Which animal did the priests put their hands on, confess the people's sins over and then send away into the desert? (goat — Lev. 16:20–22)

5. Which bird settled on Jesus' head when he was baptized? (dove — Mark 1:9–11)

6. In which creature's mouth did Peter find money to pay taxes? (fish — Matt. 17:24–27)

7. Which animal did John the Baptist say Jesus was like? (lamb — John 1:35)

8. Which animal did Jesus ride into Jerusalem? (donkey — Matt. 21:6–10)

9. Which animals did the man in Jesus' story say he wanted to plough with instead of going to the great feast? (oxen — Luke 14:19)

10. Which animal did Jesus say people would pull out of a pit on the Sabbath day? (sheep — Matt. 12:9–13)

For: 7's to 16's

(ii) Mixed question quiz with word-building on Ruth

Preparation: Prepare either letter cards or a sufficient number of newspaper headlines, scissors, paste and pieces of card. You will also need two copies of the questions and references.

Organization: Divide the children into teams and give a copy of the questions and references, Bibles, a set of the letter-cards or half the newspaper headlines, scissors, paste and card. The team which builds up all the answers first, wins.

1. Who was Ruth's mother-in-law? (Naomi – Ruth 1:3,4)
2. Where did Ruth live at first? (Moab – Ruth 1:2)
3. Where did Ruth go with her mother-in-law? (Bethlehem – Ruth 1:22)
4. What was the name of the daughter-in-law who decided to return home? (Orpah – Ruth 1:14)
5. What are the missing words in this sentence – spoken by Ruth to her mother-in-law? 'Your . . . will be my . . . and your . . . will be my . . .' (people, people, God, God – Ruth 1:16)
6. What crop was being harvested when Ruth and Naomi arrived in Bethlehem? (barley – Ruth 1:22)
7. What was the name of the relative Ruth married in the end? (Boaz – Ruth 4:13)
8. What was the name of Ruth's famous great grandson? (David – Ruth 4:17)

For: 7's to 16's

(iii) Stephen (Acts 2,6,7)

1. What was Stephen's job in the Jesus family? (He helped share out food and finances among them – Acts 6:1–5)
2. What else did Stephen do? (He preached about Jesus and performed miracles and wonders – Acts 6:8,10,14)
3. What did the people say that Stephen had said about the Temple? (That Jesus would tear it down – Acts 6:13,14)
4. How did Stephen look when he was on trial? (Unafraid/angelic – Acts 6:15)
5. What wrong did Stephen tell the people they

66

had done? (They had put Jesus to death/disobeyed God's laws – Acts 7:52,53)

6. Where was Stephen dragged to? (Outside the city – Acts 7:58)

7. What happened to Stephen then? (He was stoned – Acts 7:58)

8. At whose feet were the coats of the stone-throwers laid? (Saul – Acts 7:58)

9. What did Stephen pray just before he died? ('Lord! Do not remember this sin against them.' – Acts 7:60)

10. What do you most admire about Stephen?

h. Acrostic questions

Sometimes it is possible and helpful to contrive the answers to questions in such a way that the initial letters form a relevant word.

Suggestion:

For: 7's to 11's
Christmas

Preparation: Have a copy of the questions, answers and references below. Have also nine large pieces of card with one each of the letters of the word 'Christmas' on them.

Organization: Work as a group. As soon as a child answers a question, let him hold up the appropriate letter card. At the end, let the children re-arrange themselves into the word 'Christmas'.

1. What did the Emperor order to be taken? (census/count – Luke 2:1)

2. Where did everyone go to be registered? Everyone went to his own . . . ? (town – Luke 2:3)

3. What Empire was in power when Augustus Caesar ordered the census or counting? (Roman – Luke 2:1)

4. Who was King of Judea when Jesus was born? (Herod – Matt. 2:1)

5. Where was there no room for Mary and Joseph? (inn – Luke 2:7)

6. Who first heard the news that Jesus had been born? (shepherds – Luke 2:8)

7. Who told the shepherds about Jesus' birth? (angel – Luke 2:9)

8. Who remembered and thought deeply about all that happened that first Christmas Day? (Mary – Luke 2:19)

9. What led the wise men to Jesus and his family? (star – Matt. 2:2)

For: 7's to 16's

Joseph – Rags to Riches (Genesis 37 to 41)

Preparation: Draw the diagram, pictures and words below on board, card or acetate sheet for an overhead projector, and have suitable writing implements available.

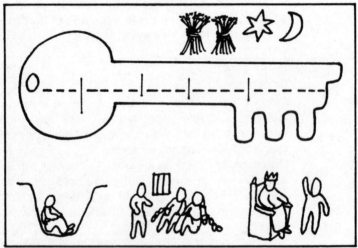

ANSWERS: Key sentence – The Lord was with Joseph.

Organization: Work as a group or divide the children into two teams, giving each team a colour. As each child answers a question correctly, let him guess a letter. If it's a letter that's in the key phrase, let him write it in (in his team's colour, if you are playing competitively). At the end, the winning team will be discovered by counting the number of letters in each colour.

1. What feeling did the brothers have for Joseph? (hate – Gen. 37:8)

68

2. Did Joseph's dreams mean that he would
   (i) leave home?
   (ii) rule over his family one day?
(ii — Gen. 37:10)
3. What did Joseph's brothers plan to do to him
first? (kill him — Gen. 37:18)
4. Which brother changed the plan? (Reuben —
Gen. 37:21)
5. Who told a lie about Joseph in Egypt? (Potiphar's wife — Gen. 39:1,7,8,16—18)
6. Which two servants of Pharaoh were in prison
with Joseph? (baker and wine steward — Gen.
40:1–3)
7. Who did Joseph say would help him to explain
their dreams? (God — Gen. 40:8)
8. Which servant had a dream that meant that
he would be put to death? (baker — Gen. 40:22)
9. How long before the butler kept his promise
to speak to Pharaoh about Joseph? (two years —
Gen. 41:1,9–12)
10. What job did Pharaoh give Joseph to do?
(collect and store grain during the seven years of
good harvests — Gen. 41:47,48).
(Key phrase: 'The Lord was with Joseph' — Gen.
39:23)

Different ways of answering questions

1. Say the answer (all age groups)

2. Write the answer (juniors and seniors)

a. Each child can write the answer on his own
piece of paper.
Examples:

Write as you listen

For: 11's to 16's

Preparation: Prepare a story, reading, song, talk,
drama or poem. Read it live or have it on a record
or cassette. Each child will need a pencil, paper
and list of questions based on the passage.
Organization: Read aloud or play the passage,
allowing plenty of time for the writing.

b. Different children in turn can write the answers on paper, card, board or acetate sheeting in front of the others.

3. Hold up answer cards (primaries and juniors)
For this you will need to have short answers, because they must be written out in duplicate on answer cards if two teams are going to compete. Add some false answer cards if you wish to make it harder for the children to select and hold up the correct answer.

4. Draw the answers (all age groups)
Either have questions whose answers can be quickly drawn by the children, or draw the answer pictures for the children and let them come and underline or tick or colour the correct answer. Draw some false answer pictures to make the quiz harder.

See page 19 for a Draw-the-Answer quiz idea and for a quiz on Joseph sold into Egypt.

Follow-on ideas for Question Quizzes

Although the suggestions below are geared to question quizzes, some of them could be adapted to follow on from other kinds of quizzes.

If a child answers a question correctly, he can be praised, or win a point for himself or his team. But there are lively ways of following on from questions and answers.

1. Noughts and crosses (7's to 16's)

(i) Noughts and crosses on a board or acetate sheet
You will need suitable writing implements and the board or acetate sheet. Draw out the noughts and crosses shape. Divide into a noughts team and a crosses team. Ask each team alternate questions. The child who guesses correctly can mark up a nought or cross. The first team to have three noughts or crosses in a vertical, horizontal or diagonal row wins a round of the contest.

(ii) Noughts and crosses with flannelgraph

Organize as in (i)

(iii) Human noughts and crosses

You will need nine chairs in three rows of three. Divide the children into noughts and crosses, and distinguish one team from another in some way, e.g. boys against girls, or one team with arm bands.

Anyone who answers a question correctly sits in one of the nine chairs. Whenever three human noughts or crosses find themselves in a row, a point is won for their team.

2. Lines and boxes (7's to 16's)

You will need a board or acetate sheet, and writing implements. Mark out your board or sheet as shown below. Divide the children into teams and give them names. Whenever a child answers a question correctly, he can join up any two dots. Whoever adds the fourth line to any little box can claim it for his team by writing his team's name inside it. At the end add up the boxes taken over by each team to find the winning team.

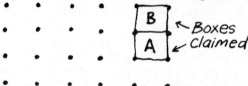

3. Snakes and ladders (5's to 16's) preferably in small groups.

You will need suitable writing implements and either card, board or acetate sheet, a dice (as large as possible), box (to shake it in), different coloured circles (for markers) and re-usable plastic adhesive or Blu-Tack. (Draw a simplified version of a Snakes and Ladders game.)

Prepare a long list of questions and divide the children into two or more teams. Each team is assigned a coloured marker. Each time a child answers a question correctly, he can shake the dice and move his team's marker accordingly. The winning team is the one that arrives 'home' first. This can take a long time to play, but you can leave it unfinished for another session.

4. Dot-to-dot shapes (5's to 11's)
You will need suitable writing implements and a board, card or acetate sheet. Think up questions on a Bible theme or story, and draw, in dot-to-dot form, something related to that theme or story. If you intend to divide the children into competing teams, you will need to draw either two identical dot-to-dot shapes or two different shapes with an identical number of dots.

A child who answers a question correctly can join up two dots. The team that completes its picture first, wins.

See page 65 for quiz on Bible Creatures.

5. Sticky paper pictures (5's to 11's)
This probably works better in smallish groups. You need scissors, sticky paper in different colours and a large sheet of card or paper over a board. From the sticky paper cut the shapes you need to build up your picture. (There must be at least as many cut-out shapes as there are questions.) You may need to sketch in some background to your picture, before the quiz starts. Ask questions on the theme of your picture and let each child who answers correctly come and add a sticky shape.

Examples:
(i) Eastern Home
Sketch in background walls and distant scenery. Prepare questions on, and have cut-out shapes of, some of the following: goat, chicken, olive trees, vine, water jars, people, bedding, low table, woman kneading or grinding, simple oven, cooking pots, broom, wine skin, lamps.

See page 96 for Bible background sources and for visual aid sources.

Eastern House

Doorway

Palm tree

crowd

man on mattress

goat

OX

stone water trough

Donkey

(ii) The paralysed man is forgiven and healed (Mark 2:1–12)

Prepare questions on, and have cut-out shapes of, some of the following: date palm tree, olive tree, vine, pomegranate tree, crowd shape, house shape, four men carrying another on a mattress, stone water trough, goat, donkey, ox.

6. Build a word, phrase or verse

You will need writing implements and large pieces of card. On these write the words of the verse or phrase, or the letters of the word you want to build up. (This must be related to the theme of your quiz.) As a child answers correctly he can hold up a letter-card or word-card. When all the letters or words have been 'won' and held up, the whole group can read the word, phrase or verse.

See page 67 for quiz on Christmas and page 19 for quiz on Joseph.

14. QUIZ IDEA
SPOT THE GAP AND FILL IT

For children competing in teams or working individually or together. You can devise them about Bible background, books, events, objects or animals, people, places, themes or

Age Groups: Primaries, Juniors, Seniors

Examples: a. **Missing words in Bible verses**

For: 7's to 16's

Preparation: Prepare verses with one or more words missing. These can be read out by you, or written up on a board. The children should have Bibles. The missing words should be words worth thinking about and the verses should be intelligible and memorable.

Examples:

'. . . has sinned.' (everyone – Rom. 3:23)

'. . . are those who work for peace; God will call them his children.' (happy – Matt. 5:9)

b. **Missing words in a Bible story**

Preparation: Prepare to tell, or have written out, a Bible story, leaving out words here and there.

Suggestion:

For: 7's to 11's

Zacchaeus (Luke 19:1–9)

This is what Zacchaeus might have written in his diary on the day he met Jesus.

'I heard that the famous teacher and healer called Jesus was coming to our town, called . . . So this morning I went out. Already there had gathered outside a large . . . I was worried that I would never manage to see Jesus because I am so . . . Then I remembered a large leafy tree by the roadside. It was a . . . tree, easy to climb. So up I went and soon found I had a great view. But I nearly fell out of that tree with shock at what happened next. Jesus stopped under the tree, looked up and said, 'Come down quickly, . . . I want to stay at your . . . So I slid down the tree and took Jesus home. I could tell people were talking about Jesus eating with a . . . like me, but Jesus had not been long in my house before I was a changed person. Until today I had cheated many people, in my job as chief . . . Now I am giving half of all I own to the . . . And to all the people I cheated I will give back . . . times as much as I took. I shall never forget today – the day Jesus changed me.'

Missing words:

1. Jericho – v.1	6. house – v.5
2. crowd – v.3	7. sinner – v.7
3. small – v.3	8. tax-collector – v.2
4. sycamore – v.4	9. poor – v.8
5. Zacchaeus – v.5	10. four – v.8.

c. Missing words in speech bubbles

Choose stories with plenty of conversation in them, and draw strip-pictures, omitting the words from the speech bubble. (See page 95 for sources of strip pictures.) The children have to fill in the missing words. If they are allowed Bibles, give them references to look up, but stress that you want them to use their own words when they write. In some quizzes, it's a good idea to write

75

the words or phrases for the speech bubbles on a separate board or sheet, in the wrong order, with some inappropriate sentences added, if you wish. *Suggestion:* Paul and Silas at Philippi (Acts 16:16–40)

For: 7's to 16's

Preparation: Draw the pictures opposite.

Organization: Work as a group or divide the children into competing teams, letting children from alternate teams take turns to come and write in the speeches.

Speeches in the correct order:
A. These men are trouble-makers!
B. Thank you, Lord Jesus, for being with us, even here.
C. Don't hurt yourself — we're all here.
D. What must I do to be saved?
E. Believe in Jesus and you and your family will be saved.
F. Let these men go.

Some inappropriate sentences which could be added for juniors:

These men have pulled down our idols.
How could you allow us to be put in prison, Lord!
Run away — everyone; we're free!
You can't teach me anything.
If you try to be good, you'll be saved.
Beat these men.

d. Missing speakers

Draw pictures as in b, but omitting the outlines and names of speakers.

Examples: Jeremiah and Ebedmelech — Jer. 38

The wise men visit Herod (for 5's to 7's) – Matt. 2:1–8

Jesus calls some followers (for 5's to 7's) – Mark 1:16–20 (opposite)

e. Unfinished story

This is a verbal quiz. Begin a Bible story that will be well known to your group. Stop at a crucial stage and ask someone to continue. If it's a long story, let several people join in, taking over from one another. For the Seniors you could make the quiz harder by telling it from the viewpoint of a minor character and by omitting certain names.

Bible verses may be treated in the same way. Stop at a crucial point and let one child finish or all the children say one word each in sequence.

f. Unfinished picture (5's to 11's)

Draw a picture or pictures of a Bible event omitting some major or minor details or leaving some

shapes only partly-drawn. The children could work as a group on one large picture or singly or in pairs on duplicated versions of a smaller picture.

Suggestion: The huge catch of fish (John 21:1–14)

For: 5's to 7's

Preparation: Make an enlarged copy of the picture and words below. Have pens, colours, gummed paper, glue.

Organization: Let the children work together to cut out and stick on fish shapes.

The huge catch of fish
Jesus told his friends to throw the net out on the right side of the boat. They obeyed and this is what happened

Jesus

Palm Sunday (Matthew 21:1–9)

For: 7's to 11's

Preparation: Draw individual copies or one large copy of the picture below and have writing implements available.

Organization: Working as a group or individually, let the children complete the unfinished picture. They may need to check in their Bibles to find out what needs to go in the picture.

Hosanna!

Blessed be the King

g. Missing verse numbers

Preparation: Write out some sentences, or draw pictures about a Bible story or events based on one chapter or passage. Box in a space by each sentence or picture so that the children can write in the appropriate verse numbers. They will need Bibles.

Suggestion: Elijah calls down fire from heaven (1 Kings 18)

For: 7's to 16's

ANSWERS: A. v.21 ; B. v.25 ; C. v.27 ; D. vv.33, 34 ; E. vv.37, 38 ; F. v.39.

15. QUIZ IDEA

SPOT THE MISTAKES – AND PUT THEM RIGHT

For children competing in teams or working individually or together. You can devise them about Bible background, events, books, objects, animals, people, places, themes or verses.

Age Groups: Primaries, Juniors, Seniors

Examples: **a. Mis-spellings**

For: 11's to 16's
You can mis-spell Bible books, names of people or places and ask the children to spell the word correctly.
Example: Jerrymia, Salms, Hakabuk (Jeremiah, Psalms, Habakkuk).

b. Mistakes in pictures

Draw strip-pictures of Bible stories or events, making deliberate mistakes in the details of the drawing, the words, the naming of the characters.
Suggestions:

The Birth of Jesus (Matthew 1,2, Luke 2)
(see opposite)

For: 5's to 7's
The Crucifixion (Matthew 26,27, Mark 14,15, Luke 22,23, John 18,19)
(see over)

ANSWERS: Corrections – A. There was no room in the inn; B. They were in a stable; C. King Herod did not pay a visit; D. The angel said the baby was in a manger; E. The shepherds and the wise men did not visit at the same time; G. Joseph was told to take the baby to Egypt.

ANSWERS: Corrections – A. Release Barabbas; B. 30 pieces of silver; C. Simon should be carrying the cross; D. Peter should be denying that he ever knew Jesus; E. Jesus should be asking God not to punish them for what they are doing; F. Peter and James did not stand near the cross.

c. Mistakes in a Bible story

Preparation: Read or paraphrase a Bible passage which includes a number of errors. If it is an unfamiliar passage you will need to read a correct version of it first.

Organization: Read the sentence or passage slowly. If you are playing competitively, award one point for spotting an error and another for saying what it should have been.

Suggestion: Peter and John and the lame man (Acts 3:1–10)

For: 11's to 16's

One day Peter and John were going to the Temple in Nazareth (Jerusalem) at the hour of prayer, which is at 11 a.m. (3 o'clock in the afternoon). A man, blind (lame) from birth, was being carried along. Every day he was put at a Temple Gate called the Wonderful Gate (Beautiful Gate), so that he could beg for food (money) from those going in or coming out of the Temple. Seeing Peter and James (John), he asked for healing (money/something). Peter looked at him and said, 'Look at me.' The man looked at them, expecting to receive something. 'I have no silver or gold,' said John (Peter). 'But I give you what I have. In the name of Jesus Christ of Capernaum (Nazareth), see (walk). And he took him by the left (right) hand and lifted him up. And after a few days his legs grew strong again. (Immediately his feet and ankles were strong.) And he went into the Temple with them, walking and leaping and praising Peter and John (God). And all the people saw this and recognized him as the man who had waited by the pool of Bethesda (at the gate of the Temple). And they were filled with wonder and amazement.

The Paralysed man (Luke 5:17–26)

For: 5's to 7's

One day Jesus was in a house talking to a lot of

people. A sick lady (man) was brought along on a bed, carried by three (some) friends. They could not get through the crowd. So they made a hole in the wall (roof) and let the sick man down to Jesus. Jesus told him his sins were not forgiven (forgiven). Then he said, 'Lie down (get up), pick up your bed and follow me (go home).'

God calls Samuel (1 Samuel 3:1–10)

For: 7's to 11's

Samuel lived in the Temple in Jerusalem with a priest called Elijah (Eli). He slept near the Ark, or special Covenant Box, but the priest slept in his own room. The priest was old but had very good eyesight (was nearly blind). Before dawn, when the lamp had gone out (before the lamp had gone out), God called Samuel. Samuel said, 'Yes, Lord (Yes, sir)!' and went to the priest saying, 'Here I am – you called me.' The priest replied, 'That's right – I did (I didn't call you).' Altogether, the Lord called Samuel five times (four times). After the third time, the priest told Samuel what to say next time God called. So when God called again, Samuel answered, 'Speak, Lord, your servant is listening' (Speak, your servant is listening.)

16. QUIZ IDEA

SWORD DRILL

You can devise Sword Drill quizzes about any Bible verse or theme, but make sure that the verses you choose to look up are intelligible to the children in the age groups involved. Give a reason for looking up a verse.

> *Examples:* Which word comes in the following verses: John 8:46, Ps. 51:2, 1 John 1:7, Rom. 6:23? – sin.
>
> Generally speaking, seniors are better able to range over the whole Bible. With Juniors, it is sometimes good to limit verses to be looked up to one passage, book or group of books.
>
> Sword Drill is the name given to the routine that accompanies looking up Bible verses. Here is one method.
>
> 1. Explain that the Bible is called a 'sword' – Eph. 6:17.
>
> 2. At the command 'Sheath your swords', the Bible is held in the right hand and placed under the left arm.
>
> 3. The leader states the theme, book, chapter and verse that he wants the children to look up – adding, 'Draw your swords.'
>
> 4. The children immediately hold the Bibles in the air and repeat the reference.
>
> 5. The leader says, 'Charge'.
>
> 6. The children open the Bibles and hunt for the verse. The first one to find it, raises his hand. When everyone (or several people) have found it, the one who had his hand up first, reads it out, or all the children read it together.

Examples: Titles for Jesus

For: 7's to 11's

> *Preparation:* Draw a large version of the diagram

below on card, black or white board or acetate sheet.

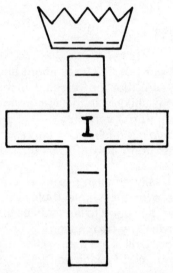

Organization: Let the children work as a group. As the answers are given, write them up on the diagram.
1. What title is given to Jesus in Luke 2 verse 11? (saviour)
2. What title is given to Jesus in Matthew 11 verse 19? (friend)
3. What title is given to Jesus in Matthew 21 verse 5? (king)

17. QUIZ IDEA

TELESCOPIC QUIZZES

These are verbal quizzes suitable for children competing in teams or working individually or together. You can devise them about Bible people, events or places. You will need an old telescope or you should make something that looks like one. Think of important Bible scenes. Picture them in your mind. As you look through the 'telescope' describe what you 'see', without giving too much away immediately.

Examples: Joseph is put in the well (Genesis 37:12–24)

For: 5's to 7's

Organization: Divide the children into teams and award points for correct guesses.

'I can see a boy walking about in the country. He looks lost. Ah, now he's talking to a man. Can't hear what the man is saying, but he's pointing. The boy hurries on. A long way ahead I can see some men and sheep. Some of the men look rather like the boy — I wonder if they're brothers. Now the boy has come up to the sheep and the men. But, oh dear, what are the men doing? They're grabbing him and the boy is struggling. Now they are pulling his coat off! And now, they're putting him down a well. The poor boy is crying and struggling . . .

The Good Samaritan (Luke 10:25–37)

For: 5's to 7's

'Oh dear! What has happened? I can see a man lying on the road. Is he ill or hurt? Hurt, I think. I wonder who hurt him? He must have been travelling somewhere. Ah, here comes someone. Surely he'll stop and help the poor man. No, he doesn't. He just walks by! How sad! But there's someone else approaching. Will he stop? Yes, no, yes, no, no! He's going by. Surely someone will help the man? Now I see someone on a donkey clip clopping up the road. I wonder whether he'll notice . . .'

The return of the Prodigal Son (Luke 15:11–24)

For: 7's to 11's

I can see an old man standing outside his house. He looks sad and he is straining to look into the distance. But what's happening now? His face is lighting up, and he's beginning to run in the direction he's been looking. And I can just see an untidy, sad-looking young man coming slowly towards him . . .'

Here are some Bible events which might be suitable for this kind of quiz:

For: 5's to 7's

David going out against Goliath. (1 Sam. 17)
Daniel in the lions' den. (Dan. 6)
Jesus healing the deaf-mute. (Mark 7)
Jesus being baptized. (Matt. 3)
The animals going into the Ark. (Gen. 7)
The Israelites crossing the sea. (Exod. 14)
Peter denying Jesus. (Matt. 26)
The angel Gabriel talking to Mary. (Luke 1)
Zacchaeus climbing down the tree and walking
home with Jesus. (Luke 19)

For: 7's to 11's

Nehemiah and his friends rebuilding the walls of
Jerusalem. (Neh. 3,4)
The Israelites marching round Jericho for the last
time as the walls start to collapse. (Joshua 6)
Jesus with bustling Martha and listening Mary.
(Luke 10)
Joseph being taken from prison and changed
ready to see Pharaoh. (Gen. 41)
Naaman dipping himself in the water for the sixth
and seventh times. (2 Kings 5)
Moses and Aaron performing a sign before
Pharaoh. (Exod. 7)
Naomi leaving Moab with her daughters-in-law.
(Ruth 1)
Peter being released from prison by an angel.
(Acts 12)

18. QUIZ IDEA
TIMED QUIZZES

For children divided into groups or panels. They can be
devised about Bible background, books, events, objects or
animals, people, places, themes or verses.

a. The minute quiz

Preparation: Devise at least 15 questions for
each panel. Have a stop-watch handy.
Organization: Ask one panel as many questions
as possible, in one minute (or however long you
wish). Award a point for each correct answer

within that time. Repeat with the other panel.
Alternatively model a quiz on a TV or radio quiz
such as Mastermind or Just a Minute.

b. Just a minute
Give a member of the group a subject to talk on
for one minute, e.g. a Bible Story or character. He
can be challenged by others if he hesitates,
repeats himself or deviates from the subject. The
challenger then takes over the subject for the
remaining seconds. Points are awarded for
successful challenges and to whoever is speaking
at the end of one minute.

19. QUIZ IDEA
TRUE OR FALSE QUIZZES

For children competing in teams or working individually or
together. True and false statements can be devised about
Bible background, books, events, objects or animals, people,
places, themes or verses.

Age Groups: Juniors, Seniors

Examples: **a. True or false – with cards**
Have cards with 'True' or 'False' on them. Give
each team a set of these and see which team
holds up the correct card first after each statement.

b. True or false – with chairs
Label two chairs 'True' or 'False' and place them
against opposite walls or in opposite corners of
the room. Bring one child from each team, in turn,
to a midway point between the chairs before
reading out each statement. Whoever sits on the
correct chair first wins a point.

For: 7's to 11's

Shadrach, Meshach and Abednego – Daniel 3
1. King Belshazzar made a golden image. (False
– it was King Nebuchadnezzar, v.1)
2. He set it up in Babylon. (True – v.1)
3. Anyone who did not worship the golden

image was to be thrown into a burning furnace. (True — v.6)

4. This image was to be worshipped once a week. (False — every time the music played, v.5)

5. Shemaiah, Meshach and Abednego refused to bow down. (False — it was Shadrach, Meshach and Abednego, v.12)

6. The king ordered the fire to be seven times hotter. (True — v.19)

7. The flames burnt up the guards. (True — v.22)

8. The king was astonished when he saw five men walking in the fire. (False — four men, v.25)

9. When the three men came out, they did not even smell of smoke. (True — v.27)

10. The king ordered that in future those who did not worship the three men would be punished. (False — those who spoke disrespectfully of Shadrach, Meshach and Abednego's God would be punished, v.29)

For: 8's to 11's

Christian Missionaries

1. Christian missionaries go to other countries to tell people about Jesus. (True)

2. Christian missionaries find it easier to follow Jesus than other Christians. (False — they are like the rest of us)

3. Christian missionaries are ordinary people like us. (True)

4. Paul was the only New Testament missionary. (False — Peter, Barnabas and others were also N.T. missionaries)

5. Every Christian should go overseas. (False)

6. No Christian should go overseas. (False)

7. Several missionaries have gone out from this church. (True — hopefully!)

8. Money drops from heaven for missionaries. (False)

9. Christian missionaries need our support. (True)

10. English-speaking countries don't need missionaries. (False)

If you are competing, you may want to award a point for the correct answer and another if the children can give a reason (if it's false) or expand a little (if it's true).

20. QUIZ IDEA

WORD-BUILDING QUIZZES

For children competing in teams. Children can be asked to build a word, phrase or sentence relating to Bible background, books, events, objects or animals, people, places, themes or verses.

Age Groups: Juniors, Seniors

Examples: **a. Spell out Bible names**
Preparation: Write out the Bible names you want the children to spell out, on large-squared paper, one letter per square. Do this twice if you are going to have two teams.
Organization: Give the teams the sets of jumbled letters. Ask them to spell out as many Bible names (of people, places or books) as they can, perhaps within a certain time.

b. Spell out a Bible verse
Prepare as above.

c. Spell out words on a theme (11's to 16's)
Prepare as in 1, having thought out a relevant theme.
Some suggestions:
Spell out as many adjectives as you can which describe Jesus' character.
Spell out the fruits of the Spirit — Gal. 5:22

d. Spell out the answers to questions
For: 7's to 16's
The children can spell out the answers with letter-cards or with newspaper letters. For the latter, you will need card, scissors, paste and brushes, and a good supply of newspapers with plenty of bold headings.
Pasting cut-out newspaper letters onto card, is

fiddly and time-consuming, so devise questions with one word answers, or using the sort of words that children can cut out whole.

Examples:

What was the feeling that Cain had for Abel? (hate)

The story of the Prodigal Son teaches us that God is like a loving . . . what? (father)

See page 65 for word-building quiz on Ruth.

Useful addresses and sources

1. Sources of visual aids

Overhead projectors, acetate sheets and markers may be obtained from National Audio-Visual Aid Centre, 254–256, Belsize Road, London N.W.6. or

Vision Screen Services, Riversdale House, North Fambridge, Chelmsford, Essex.

Felt pens and markers may be obtained from W. H. Smiths, Woolworths and any stationers.

Cheap sources of paper include the reverse side of wallpaper and lining paper.

2. Sources of pictures

Society for Promoting Christian Knowledge, Holy Trinity Church, Marylebone Road, London N.W.1. (Series: Christian Year Pictures 21 x 14 inches)

National Christian Education Council, Robert Denholm House, Nuffield, Redhill, Surrey. (5 series of 12 pictures per pack; large maps; 10 drawings of life in Bible times by Donald Grey)

Church Information Office, Church House, Dean's Yard, London SW1P 3NZ. (Set of 11 O.T. and 11 N.T. pictures 380 x 280 mm. in brilliant colour)

Concordia Publishing House, 117–123 Golden Lane, London EC1Y OTL. (Set of 6 pictures $6\frac{1}{2}$ x $4\frac{1}{2}$ inches)

Bible Lands Society, High Wycombe, Bucks. (Set of coloured photos of the Holy Land)

Christian Literature Crusade, The Dean, Alresford, Hants. SO24 9BJ. (Series of 10 Giant Flannelgraphs)

Hulton Educational Publications, Raans Road, Amersham, Bucks HP6 6JJ. (3 blackboard maps of Palestine. Acetate sheets are available to take chinagraph pencil markings)

Globe Education Equipment, Houndhills, Basingstoke, Hants. (Map of Holy Land 122 x 91 cm. Can be chalked on)
A. Wheaton and Co., Educational Publishers, Hennock Road, Exeter EX2 8RP (Visual N.T. map of the Holy Land 67 x 49 cm.; Map of the world of the O.T. 47 x 67 cm.; Wall map of the Holy Land 168 x 215 cm.)

3. Picture strip story books

'The Real Jesus' (S.U.); 'The Picture Bible for all ages' Vols. 1–6, covering whole Bible (S.U.); 'Stranger than Fiction' (C.L.C.); Comics: 'Abraham', 'Jesus Power,' 'The Acts', 'The birth of a Saviour' (Australian Bible Society)

4. Sources of music

Records and cassettes can be obtained from some music shops, most Christian book shops and
Pilgrim Records, 1, Bath Street, London EC1V 9QA.
Musical Gospel Outreach, 33, West Hill, Wandsworth, London SW18 1RB.
Salvationist Publishing and Supplies Ltd., 117, Judd Street, London WC1H 9NN.
Reflection, 26, Eastbourne Avenue, London W3 6JN.
Dovetail Records, 10, Seaforth Avenue, New Malden, Surrey KT3 6JP.
E.M.I. Records Ltd., Hayes, Middlesex.
Hallmark Records, Victoria Works, Edgware Road, London N.W.1.

Suitable records and cassettes – music only

The Christmas Festival in brass (S.A. band) – SXLP 50016.
Tijuana Christmas – MFP 1266.
Hallelujah Brass – WST 9544.
Peter Jackson – WST 9506.
Peter Jackson Instant Piano series Vol.1 – SAC 5030.
Peter Jackson, Favourite hymns played on the piano – WC5089 (Cas.).
Family Favourites – SAC 5089.
Derek Moon plays for you – Sharon 302; Cassette – PC 834.
Jack Ward, Sankey's Favourites – QLPS 19.
Jack Ward, Sankey Medley – QLPS 21.
Jack Ward, The Twilight Hour – SAC 5062.
Marching with Jesus – GES 1094.

Suitable records and cassettes – words and music

The World of Christmas – SPA/A 104.
Christmas Music, The Royal Choral Society and Orchestra – ECS 243.
Carolling with the London Emmanual Choir – PC 838 (Cas.).
Ralph Carmichael, Christmas Joys – LS 7041.

Sing-a-long songs No.2, Children's Bible Hour Choir – PC 827 (Cas.).
Hymns for little children – MFP.
Praise Him with melody – BAB 3508.
Burl Ives sings with the children – SAC 5072.
Favourite songs for little children – SRS 5048.
Joyful sounds unto the Lord – TCFTN 2503 (Cas.).
Great hymns, Huddersfield Choral Society – ECSR 210L.
The Bill Gaither trio – KL 034.
20 Best Loved Hymns, London Emmanuel Choir – 311 887 (Cas.).
Here is Youth Praise – Falcon records.
Prepare ye the way, Parts 1 and 2 – LPSS 3/4; Cassette – CSS 3/4.
Come together – LS 7006; Cassette – LC 7006.
If my people – LS 7022; Cassette – LC 7022.

5. Books

Bible background books:
'Animals, birds and plants of the Bible', Ladybird.
'Life in the time of Jesus', Margaret Boys, Hodder and Stoughton.
'Life in the time of Paul', Margaret Boys, Hodder and Stoughton.
'Discovering the Biblical world', Frank Harry Thomas, Hodder and Stoughton.
'The Bible as History', Werner Keller.
'Animals, birds and plants of the Bible', Willard Smith, Hodder and Stoughton.
'Animals of Bible lands', George Cansdale, Paternoster Press.
'Insight into Bible times and customs', G. Christian Weiss.
'Encyclopedia of the Bible', Lion Publishing.

Books to help with visual aids:
'Photo-guide to the Old Testament', Wiseman, Lion.
'Photo-guide to the New Testament', Green, Lion.
'Bible buildings', Elphinstone, Fyffe.
'Palestine models', Elphinstone, Fyffe.
'Christmas cut-outs', Anne Cotton, Lion.
'Visual Aid Encyclopaedia'. (Information for making over 350 visual aids. Available at C.L.C.)
'Sketching and Telling', Keith Thomson, Victory Press

Other useful books:
'Baker's Dictionary of Theology', Pickering and Inglis.
A concordance.
'The New Bible Dictionary', Inter-Varsity Press